BLAST OFF!
EARTH

Helen and David Orme

North American edition copyright © ticktock Entertainment Ltd 2009
First published in North America in 2009 by ticktock Media Ltd.,
The Old Sawmill, 103 Goods Station Road,
Tunbridge Wells, Kent, TN1 2DP, U.K.

ticktock project editor: Julia Adams
ticktock project designer: Emma Randall

We would like to thank: Sandra Voss, Tim Bones, James Powell,
Indexing Specialists (U.K.) Ltd.

ISBN-13: 978-1-84898-159-1 pbk

Printed in China
9 8 7 6 5 4 3 2 1

Picture credits (t=top; b=bottom; c=center; l=left; r=right; bg=background):
Corbis: 15bl, 21tl. NASA: 13bl, 21br. Science Photo Library: 4/5bg (original). Shutterstock: front cover, 1tl, 1br, 2/3bg, 8b, 9tl, 9tr,
9cr, 9br, 11b, 12b, 16c, 18b, 19bl, 22cl, 24bg. ticktock picture archive: 5tr, 6bl, 6/7bg, 7tr, 7b, 10bl, 10/11bg, 11tl, 13tr, 14bl,
14/15bg, 15tr, 17tr, 17bl, 17br, 18/19bg, 19tr, 20c, 22cr, 22/23bg, 23tl, 23bl, 23br.

Every effort has been made to trace the copyright holders, and we apologize in advance for any unintentional omissions.
We would be pleased to insert the appropriate acknowledgments in any subsequent edition of this publication.

Contents

Where is Earth? 4–5

Planet Facts 6–7

Life on Earth 8–9

What's the Weather Like? . . . 10–11

Changing Temperatures . . . 12–13

Earth's Crust 14–15

On the Surface 16–17

The Moon and Satellites . . . 18–19

Earth in History 20–21

Exploring Earth 22–23

Glossary and Index 24

Where is Earth?

There are eight planets in our **solar system**. The planets travel around the Sun. Earth is the third planet from the Sun.

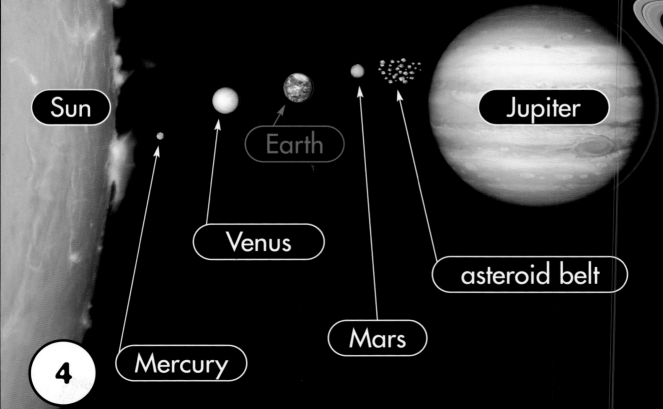

Sun

Earth

Jupiter

Venus

asteroid belt

Mars

Mercury

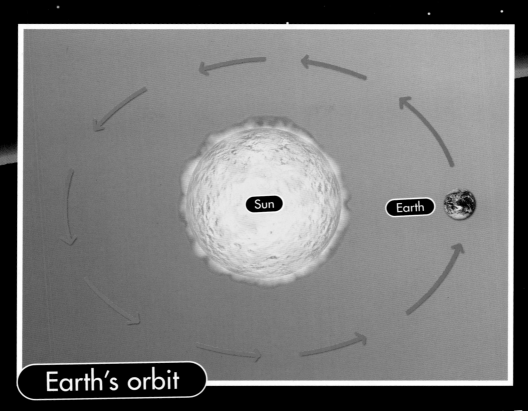

Earth's orbit

Earth travels around the Sun once every 365 days. This journey around the Sun is called Earth's **orbit**. The time a planet takes to orbit the Sun once is called a year.

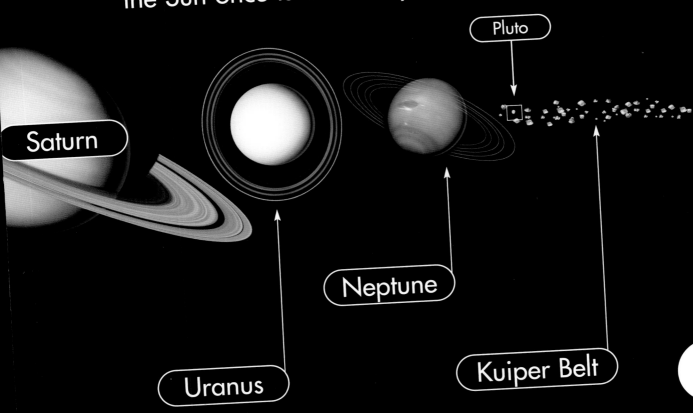

Saturn

Uranus

Neptune

Pluto

Kuiper Belt

Planet Facts

Earth is the only known planet in our **solar system** with **liquid** water on its surface. Over three fourths of our planet is covered by water.

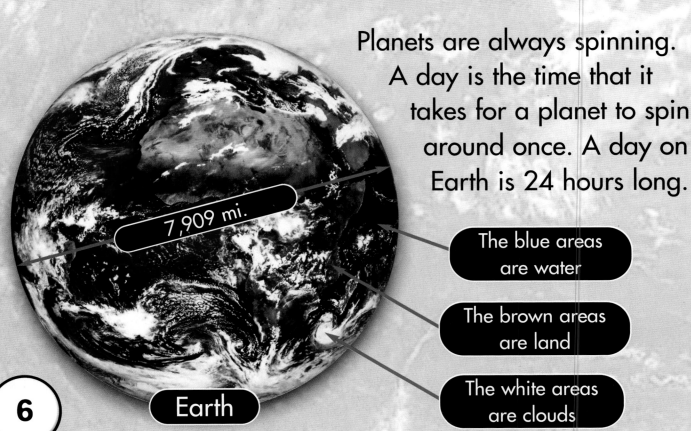

Planets are always spinning. A day is the time that it takes for a planet to spin around once. A day on Earth is 24 hours long.

7,909 mi.

Earth

The blue areas are water

The brown areas are land

The white areas are clouds

daytime

nighttime

This artwork shows Earth as it spins around. One half of the planet faces away from the Sun. It is in the dark. The other half is in the sunlight.

Earth has two places called poles: the North Pole and the South Pole. These are at the top and bottom of the planet. The Sun does not shine very strongly at the poles, so they are cold and icy all year round.

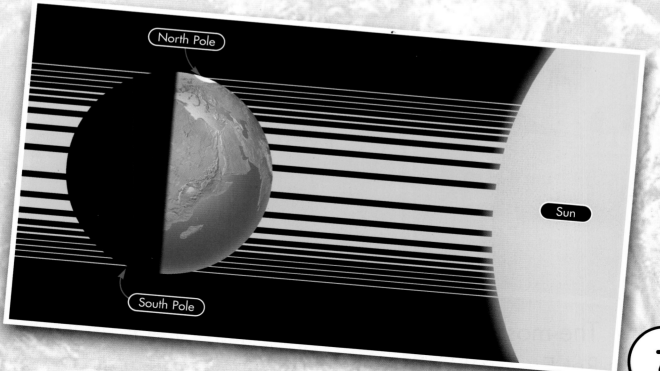

North Pole

South Pole

Sun

Life on Earth

Earth is the only planet we know about where people, animals, and plants can live. Life is possible on Earth because it has **liquid** water.

The most important thing needed for life is water. But Earth is perfect for life in other ways, too.

Earth has an **atmosphere** with **oxygen**. Almost all living things need oxygen in order to breathe and survive.

Some places on Earth have very extreme temperatures. But most of Earth is neither too hot nor too cold for life.

0°C (140°F)
0°C (122°F)
0°C (104°F)
30°C (86°F)
20°C (68°F)
10°C (50°F)
0°C (32°F)
10°C (14°F)
-20°C (-4°F)
0°C (-22°F)
0°C (-40°F)
0°C (-58°F)
0°C (-76°F)
0°C (-94°F)
C (-112°F)
C (-130°F)

The hottest place on Earth is Al 'Aziziyah, Libya, in Africa. Temperatures can get up to 58°C (136°F) there.

This is 0°C (32°F). It is the temperature when water freezes.

The coldest temperatures are in Antarctica. Once the temperature went down to -89°C (-128°F) there!

What's the Weather Like?

The layer of gases that make up Earth's **atmosphere** is called air. It covers the planet. Because air moves around, we have different types of weather in different places.

When the air moves, we have wind. The wind can be very powerful. Along with water, the wind has made this rock into a strange shape by wearing it away.

Strong winds can cause a lot of damage to buildings and trees.

Wind also moves clouds around the planet. Clouds are made up of millions of very tiny water droplets. These droplets can join together to make bigger drops. If these drops get big and heavy enough, they fall down as rain.

Changing Temperatures

Earth is perfect for life, because it is not too hot and too cold. But scientists think that the **temperatures** on Earth are changing.

smoke with carbon dioxide

When we burn oil or coal, we make a gas called **carbon dioxide**. The amount of this gas in our **atmosphere** is growing.

Carbon dioxide trapped in Earth's atmosphere stops heat from escaping from Earth. Scientists think that the trapped gases will slowly make Earth heat up.

atmosphere

heat waves

surface

Temperature change has already happened on the planet Venus. This planet has heated up so much that it is much too hot and dry for life.

Earth's Crust

Planet Earth is a huge ball of rock. It is made of four layers. The center of Earth is called its core. The inside of the planet is very hot.

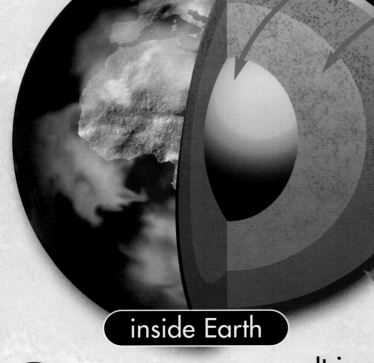

inside Earth

Earth has an inner and an outer core. They are mostly made of **iron**. The inner core is the hottest part of Earth.

This layer is called the mantle. It is made of red-hot rock. Some of it is **molten rock**.

The crust of Earth is the part that we live on. It is made up of land and oceans. It floats on top of the mantle.

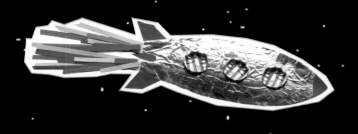

Earth's crust is split into sections called **plates**. The plates are moving very slowly all the time.

The red lines on the map above show the edges of the plates. They fit together like a jigsaw puzzle!

Sometimes, when the plates move, Earth shakes so much that the ground shudders and cracks. We call this an earthquake.

On the Surface

Earth's surface is covered in mountains and valleys. Earth's highest mountain is Mount Everest. It is 29,028 feet high!

Mount Everest is so high, that its top is sometimes higher than the clouds!

Mountains are made by the movement of Earth's **plates**. When two plates push against each other, they sometimes create a mountain by pushing up layers of rock. This is how Mount Everest was created. It takes millions of years for this to happen.

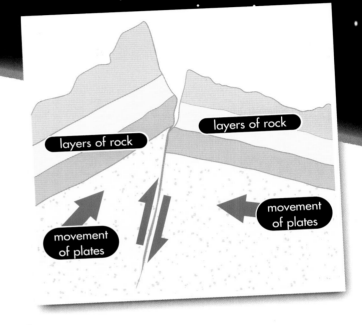

layers of rock

layers of rock

movement of plates

movement of plates

molten rock

volcano

plates

Sometimes, when Earth's plates move, an opening appears in the crust. The hot, **molten rock** from inside Earth bursts to the surface. This is called a volcano.

The Moon and Satellites

The Moon is a big rock that **orbits** Earth. Objects that orbit a planet are called **satellites**. The Moon is Earth's only natural satellite.

As seen from Earth, the Moon is the brightest object in the **solar system** after the Sun. We can see it without a telescope.

Earth has many other satellites. These satellites have been launched into space by rockets. They have many different uses.

satellite being launched on a rocket

satellite orbiting Earth

Satellites are used to show television shows and connect cell phone calls. Some satellites can give us information about Earth's weather and warn us about **hurricanes**.

Earth in History

Hundreds of years ago, most people believed that Earth was flat. They believed that you could fall off the edge of Earth!

edge of Earth

This map shows Europe and where people believed the edge of Earth was.

Europe

map from 1492

When **astronomers** saw that the other planets were round, they realized that Earth had to be round, too.

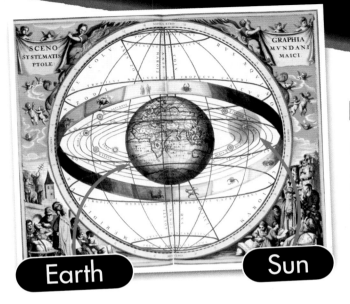

Earth

Sun

People also used to think that the Sun went around Earth. Today, we know that it is the other way around.

This picture was painted in 1660, more than 300 years ago. It shows the Sun **orbiting** Earth.

With space travel and the use of satellites, we can see that Earth orbits around the Sun. This photograph of Earth was taken in 1968 by **astronauts** traveling to the Moon.

Moon's surface

Exploring Earth

We **still** don't know everything there is to know about Earth. But **satellites** and **robots** help us find out more about our planet.

Sahara Desert

Satellites can take photographs of wide areas of land. This helps us make very exact maps of large regions of Earth. It also allows us to see what Earth looks like from space.

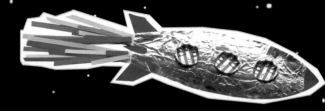

Robots can be used to explore and take pictures of the deepest parts of the ocean.

Some robots look for **oil** and **minerals**.

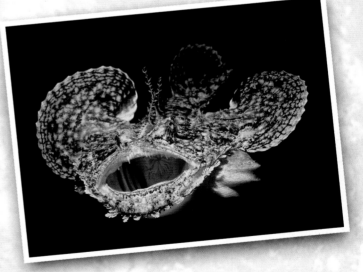

Some robots can study animals that live in the deepest oceans, such as this fish.

Glossary

Asteroid A rocky object that orbits the Sun. Most asteroids orbit the Sun between Mars and Jupiter.

Astronaut A person trained to travel or work in space.

Astronomer A person who studies space, often using telescopes.

Atmosphere The gases that surround a star, planet, or moon.

Carbon dioxide A gas that is made when something burns.

Hurricane The largest, strongest storm on Earth. It forms over an ocean, and its high winds join in a circle.

Iron A very hard and strong metal.

Liquid Something that flows easily.

Minerals Material from Earth that is not a plant or an animal. Gold, silver, iron, and salt are all minerals.

Molten rock Rock that has been melted and flows like a liquid.

Oil A greasy liquid that many machines need in order to work.

Orbit The path that a planet or other object takes around the Sun, or the path a satellite takes around a planet.

Oxygen One of the gases in Earth's atmosphere that we breathe. People and animals need oxygen to live.

Plates The separate pieces that make up Earth's crust. They float very slowly over liquid rock.

Satellite A moon or a man-made object that is in orbit around a planet.

Solar system The Sun and everything that is in orbit around it.

Temperature How hot or cold something is.

Index

atmosphere 9–10, 12–13

carbon dioxide 12–13

core of Earth 14

earthquakes 15

history of Earth 20–21

hurricanes 19

iron 14

life on Earth 8

molten rock 14

Moon 18, 21

orbits 5, 18, 21

oxygen 9

planets 4–5

plates 15, 17

poles (North/South) 7

robots 22

satellites 18–19, 22

solar system 6, 18

Sun 4–5, 21

surface of Earth 13, 16

temperatures 9, 12–13

volcanoes 17

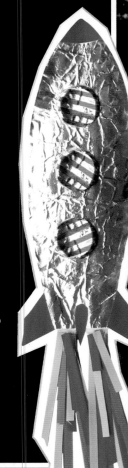

BLAST OFF!
Let's Explore
EARTH

Blast off to space and explore our solar system!
Including the recent addition of the dwarf planets, this series offers
a fun-to-read insight into the solar system supported by superb
NASA photography and artwork, as well as high-quality
graphics explaining complicated scientific concepts
in an engaging and accessible way.

Each book includes:
- A map of the solar system
- Planet facts, measurements, and special features
- Weather facts and what's on the surface
- History of discoveries
- Space missions in the past, present, and future

ISBN 978 1 84898 159 1

9 781848 981591

T4-ALW-379

4. Excavation of the Villa of Publius Fannius Synistor, Boscoreale, with Mount Vesuvius in the distance, ca. 1901. Room C is at the far right, with Room D and then Room 24 to its left (see fig. 13).

to a great height in the form of a tall trunk, which spread out at the top as though into branches. . . . Occasionally it was brighter, occasionally darker and spotted, as it was either more or less filled with earth and cinders.") The layer just above the Avellino eruption (about 3500 B.C.) shows the successive presence of pens for domesticated animals and plow furrows. Above that are two more paleosols (layers of fossilized soil) with vestiges of crossed and ridge-and-furrow plowing also from the Bronze Age. And a layer dating perhaps to the Iron Age (about the tenth to the ninth century B.C.) preserves traces of cart tracks that run northwest to southeast.

These successive strata of human presence can today be connected with other evidence recently discovered both on the eventual site of Pompeii and beyond it. An especially large excavation at Longola in the territory of Poggiomarino has uncovered a village of buildings on piles built along the Sarno.[7] It dates originally to the late Bronze Age or early Iron Age, and it was inhabited from the late second or early first millennium B.C. until approximately the time Pompeii was founded in the late seventh or early sixth century B.C. A still fragmentary picture

has begun to emerge of a difficult environment that was constantly being changed by volcanic eruptions but was used continuously by human beings, who found there a place to build both their settlements and a livelihood.

Although it cannot be associated with specific excavation data, more abundant archaeological evidence exists for the broad period stretching from the seventh to the second century B.C. The material comes from two pre-Roman necropoleis in the area of Boscoreale, one in the village of Spinelli, less than a mile northeast of Pompeii, and the other from near Marchesa, a little over three miles northeast of the city, and perhaps from a third burial ground in the hamlet of Pisanella (see figs. 5, 6).[8] The concentration of objects from the seventh and sixth centuries B.C. is especially interesting. This material, which includes impasto and bucchero ceramics, imported Greek vases, and Italic geometric pottery, suggests the presence of two villages that were part of the indigenous culture of the Sarno Valley that nurtured, probably through consolidation, the birth of Pompeii.[9] The discovery of South Italian red-figured ceramics and Gnathia ware derived from Greek

5

7

6

8

5–6. Two proto-Corinthian aryballoi and an Etrusco-Corinthian cup from a necropolis near Boscoreale. 7th–6th century B.C. Clay, h. of each 2⅜ in. (6 cm). Antiquarium, Boscoreale (57, 24, 179)

7–8. Votive offerings from a 4th-century tomb on the Via Chiesa, Boscotrecase. Terracotta; female head: h. 3¾ in. (9.5 cm), bird: h. 3⅝ in. (9.3 cm). Antiquarium, Boscoreale (37, 93)

prototypes in a fourth-century tomb on the Via Chiesa in Boscotrecase seems to indicate that some of these villages continued to exist for some time after the foundation of the city. The presence of votive items like small cups and statuettes (see figs. 7, 8) suggests, furthermore, that there were rural sanctuaries here in the late Classical and Hellenistic periods (ca. 490–90 B.C.). Until now such sanctuaries were known only to the south of Pompeii, at Fondo Iozzino, Bottaro, and Sant'Abbondio, but they must also have existed in the large area on the slopes of Mount Vesuvius.

The picture that has emerged of this landscape now also includes information about the pre-Roman period that comes from the first systematic excavation of the agricultural terrain around the farmhouse at Villa Regina in Boscoreale. The evidence there includes a ceramic fragment from the Archaic period (ca. 575–490 B.C.) and about thirty others that date from the end of the fourth to the second century B.C. They indicate the presence of agricultural activity in this area from at least the Samnite period, and this data is confirmed by evidence of a Samnite phase (dating to the second rather than the third century B.C.) in the building history of the Villa dei Misteri, about a half mile northwest of Pompeii.[10] The strongest, albeit indirect, evidence of agricultural activity in this area during the pre-Roman period is the discovery that the farmland was sectioned off into what was a true *limitatio*, long before

the Romans used the term. This can be deduced from observing the alignment of the Via di Mercurio and the urban plan of Regio VI in Pompeii with the planimetric axes of certain villas, for example the Villa dei Misteri and the Villa di Diomede, that are known to have existed before the establishment of the Roman colony in 81 B.C. The dating of the Villa di Diomede to before 81 B.C. is based on the fact that its northern side is bisected by the construction, certainly in the early colonial period, about 81–70 B.C., of the so-called Via delle Tombe, which leaves the northwest corner of the city through the Porta Ercolano.[11]

All this confirms that the land that extends from the north side of Pompeii and up the slopes of Vesuvius was populated in the prehistoric and Archaic periods and was cultivated systematically before the founding of Sulla's Roman colony at Pompeii. A date at the end of the fourth or beginning of the third century B.C.—which corresponds with an important phase in the urban development of Pompeii—is plausible based on material excavated in the area around Villa Regina.[12] How far this agricultural division (a Samnitic *limitatio*) extended is not known. The farmhouse of Villa Regina, which dates to the colonial period, is included in it, but no equally useful information has come down from the earlier, private excavations. In other areas on the volcano's slopes—Torre del Greco–Herculaneum, Terzigno, San Giuseppe, Ottaviano, and Somma Vesuviana—settlements of farmhouses existed at relatively high altitudes (about 650 to 1,000 feet above sea level) on rises separated by the beds of streams that flowed from the base of the volcano's cone. One of them, at Somma Vesuviana, had a portico with tufa columns and four-sided Italic-Ionic capitals that dates to the end of the second or the beginning of the first century B.C. An inscription in Oscan, the language of the Samnites, from the area of Somma Vesuviana also documents the presence of a public road that traveled up the mountain.[13] Even though the inscription probably pertains to the *territorium* of Nola, north of Vesuvius, rather than Pompeii, it is without doubt evidence of a system of public roads in this area as early as the Samnite period (second century B.C.). It might even refer specifically to a section of road that came from Pompeii and followed a route on the mountainside that was later replicated by a modern, still existing thoroughfare.

Later archaeological evidence from the Roman period (first century B.C. to A.D. 79) indicates that these country houses were almost all dedicated to producing wine (and to a lesser extent olive oil), which would probably also have been the area's principal product in earlier times.[14] Evidence of locally made amphorae for wine survives from as early as the Hellenistic era, or the fourth to second century B.C. A varietal originally from Sicily (where it was called *Murgentina*) was grown so profusely in the region that it came to be called *Vitis pompeiana*. In the first century both Columella (*On Agriculture* 3.2.10, 27) and Pliny the Elder (*Natural History* 14.22, 25, 34, 35) noted that *Gemina minor*, a grape from the Aminea family, flourished on Mount Vesuvius as well as on the hills around Sorrento and despite its limited production was judged to be the best in the world.[15] They also mentioned *Vitis holconia*, named for one of Pompeii's most prominent families, and *Vitis vennuncula*, which was found in the area between Sorrento and Pompeii as well. Both had good yields but were of middling quality, equal to *Murgentina* in the classification of ancient wines.

This evidence confirms the importance of wine making in the area around Pompeii from at least the late Samnite period (fourth to second century B.C.), a fact that is reiterated by the important presence of the cult of Dionysus at Pompeii: there was, for example, a sanctuary dedicated to the god of wine at Sant'Abbondio from at least the late Samnite period and perhaps earlier. Although the famous painting from the *lararium*, a shrine for holding images of household gods, in the Casa del Centenario in Pompeii that shows Dionysus standing before a vine-covered mountain has been called into question, the literary sources that describe Vesuvius as a mountain crowned almost to its summit with grapevines cannot be doubted. The vines were so plentiful that Spartacus's soldiers used ropes made of vines to escape from the Roman soldiers who had trapped them on the mountain.[16]

Even if the presses, wine cellars, and agricultural tools uncovered by the early, private excavations around Pompeii were not what they were looking for, these objects provide abundant information about the production methods at these country estates at the time of Vesuvius's eruption in A.D. 79. More recent excavations like the one at Villa Regina offer irrefutable evidence of the classic arrangement

9. Lever press used in wine making in the Villa dei Misteri, Pompeii, reconstructed ca. 1932

of grape vines supported by stakes. Ample written sources also record the details of grape cultivation, from the dates of the harvests to the type of wine produced and the number of stakes available.

Several of the rural complexes offer evidence that in addition to agricultural buildings they included at least part-time residences for the landowners. The houses were furnished with baths, porticoes, *triclinia* (formal dining rooms), and mosaic and painted decorations, some of great artistry and quality like the frescoes in what is called the Second Style of Roman painting (ca. 60–20 B.C.) in the Villa dei Misteri, the Villa of P. Fannius Synistor, and the villa at Terzigno and the Third Style frescoes (ca. 20 B.C.–A.D. 20) at the Villa of Agrippa Postumus at Boscotrecase (several of which are also in the Metropolitan Museum). Decorative sculpture found at some of these villas indicates that as early as the first colonial period and perhaps also in the Samnite era (third to second century B.C.) they were more than just housing for agricultural workers and that the landowners lived in them for large amounts of time. Literary sources also tell of absentee owners, Roman aristocrats like Cicero or Agrippa Postumus, who had bought older villas, probably the ones with the best views, and remodeled or adapted them to be used for their leisure. Yet these cases were definitely in the minority. Pompeii was nowhere near as popular or influential as Puteoli (modern Pozzuoli) or Cumae (Cuma), to the north near Naples, and the countryside around Pompeii was not Baiae (Baia), where rich and famous Romans flocked to bathe in the healing waters of the Phlegraean Fields. Some of the owners of the country houses north of Pompeii were certainly illustrious Roman nobles who sought out the peace and quiet of the countryside, but the majority of those who decorated the walls of their residences with Second Style

paintings must have been prominent members of the new local colonial aristocracy. The houses ranged from the humblest agricultural residences to grand vacation villas. At one end of the scale was Villa Regina, which had only one *triclinium* in addition to the areas for living and wine production. At the other was the villa said to have been used by Poppaea Sabina, the emperor Nero's second wife, in Oplontis (modern Torre Annunziata), where the original *torcularium*, or wine pressing room, was greatly reduced in size to make room for residential quarters near the swimming pool. There were very few houses like Poppaea's villa in the region, however, and most of those were located along the coast. Certainly some villas were designed from the outset for pleasure rather than as working farms and were really pseudo urban villas. One example is the Villa dei Papiri at Herculaneum; if there was any agricultural activity there it involved raising fish. And unlike what happened at Oplontis, the owners of the Villa dei Misteri not only jealously preserved their old and splendid wall paintings but also maintained the villa's original function as a place to make wine (see fig. 9). It is a great pity that the villa's wine cellars have never been completely excavated.

The relatively modest dimensions of the majority of these villa complexes and their very numbers across this area (at Cava Ranieri, for example, in the hamlet of Boccia al Mauro near Terzigno, at least four farmhouses have been identified) indicate that they were the centers of relatively small farms.[17] Originally it was thought that the average size of these farms was 100 *iugeri* (about 60 acres), an area calculated on the basis of the number and capacity of the *dolia*, or

wine jars, found in their cellars. This estimate, however, has been called into question with the excavation at Villa Regina, where there were only eighteen *dolia* and a vineyard estimated at 17 *iugeri*.

How was this landscape dotted with villas configured? As evidence accumulates, the area seems more and more likely to have been what the Greek geographer and historian Strabo (ca. 63 B.C.–after A.D. 21) described in his *Geography* (5.4, 8) as a "continuous succession of buildings and cultivated fields." It has been assumed that this valuable economic region corresponded to the *pagus*, or district, called Augustus Felix Suburbanus in Pompeiian inscriptions, including one that attributes to its inhabitants the construction of a bank of seats in the amphitheater. Yet the case is not so clear and rests on inductive reasoning. Even if this *pagus* did exist as early as the Samnite period, it was certainly renamed along with the rest of the city when the new Roman colony was dedicated. Furthermore, though *Felix* (Latin for "happy," "fortunate," or "prosperous") was the epithet of Lucius Cornelius Sulla, the Roman conqueror of Pompeii, it would also have accurately described the fertility of the area. The other valuable Pompeiian territory, the coastal area including the port, was very likely called, as is suggested in inscriptions, (*pagus*) Saliniensis, or the Salt Makers District.

The eruption of A.D. 79 buried the city of Pompeii along with all of the surrounding territory. The villas, vineyards, orchards, and gardens, with their famous Pompeiian onions, all ended up under many feet of pumice and gray mud. The desolation of the countryside lasted only briefly, however. Although the city was not reconstructed, the land, now divided between Nocera and Nola, was returned to cultivation,[18] in part thanks to the fertile volcanic soil so well known to the ancients and extolled by both Strabo (*Geography* 5.4.3) and Pliny the Elder (*Natural History* 18.110–11).[19] Here and there new villas, some of them luxurious, were erected on the outcroppings of ancient ruins (see fig. 10), but they looked out over a completely changed landscape. The new road built in the second century ran straight across the fields that now covered Pompeii, and for a long time the coast, with its once crowded port and sumptuous seaside villas owned by wealthy Romans, remained deserted and silent.

New Perspectives on the
Villa of Publius Fannius Synistor at Boscoreale

BETTINA BERGMANN

A s the grass grows over a deserted excavation, so the facts which come to light with an archaeological discovery are quickly overgrown with errors and insecure memories, if they are not immediately recorded," Otto Brendel wrote in his review of Phyllis Williams Lehmann's *Roman Wall Paintings from Boscoreale in the Metropolitan Museum of Art*. "This, therefore, is a very useful publication," Brendel continued. "For the first time the *disjecta membra* of the villa of Fannius Synistor are exhibited together in good illustrations, and with well documented descriptions."[20] Published fifty-three years after the villa was dismantled and reburied in 1900, Lehmann's magisterial study remains unsurpassed for its meticulous observations and exhaustive iconographic research, through which she revealed the richness of the illusionistic frescoes. The nineteen fresco sections that were the subject of her book had instantly

engaged the public when they went on display at the Metropolitan Museum in 1906, and they remain today among the most famous and paradoxical of Roman paintings.

In the half century since Lehmann's study, grass has indeed grown over the Villa of Publius Fannius Synistor, and facts have become obscured. Yet knowledge has also advanced. In 1987 Maxwell Anderson published (in an issue of the Metropolitan's *Bulletin*) an axonometric rendering that showed, through black-and-white line drawings, the location of the various frescoes throughout the rooms. Since then, numerous excavations, articles, and exhibitions have enriched and altered our knowledge of social life in the Roman region called Campania, most notably the discoveries of the elaborate seaside villa at Oplontis (modern Torre Annunziata, less than two miles west of Pompeii), whose frescoes suggest a common workshop; the

11–12. Frescoes of Room H in the Villa of P. Fannius Synistor, Boscoreale, ca. 1900 (see also fig. 41). Photographs: Antikensammlung, Berlin

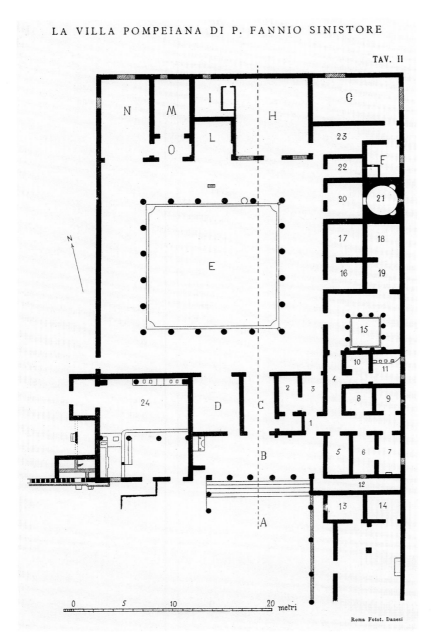

TAV. II

Roma Fotot. Danesi

13. Felice Barnabei (Italian, 1842–1922). *La Villa Pompeiana di P. Fannio Sinistore,* 1901

smaller, rustic Villa Regina at Boscoreale; the three villas at nearby Terzigno; and similar architectural frescoes at Baia and on the Palatine Hill in Rome. Scholarly work on contemporary dwellings such as the Villa dei Misteri and the Casa del Labirinto in Pompeii offers a wealth of comparative material. Despite evident similarities between these sites, every room in every villa possesses a distinctive character.

The impetus for this publication was the conservation of the Metropolitan Museum panels for the purpose of their installation in the new Greek and Roman Galleries that opened in 2007. In the process, further aspects of the painted walls emerged, and it was decided to bring the potential of modern technology to these insights, as well as to the fundamental picture drawn by Lehmann, by constructing a virtual model of the Villa of P. Fannius Synistor. All Roman frescoes were, of course, inseparable parts of a building. Since a physical reunification of the surviving fragments will likely never happen, only through a virtual model can one imagine experiencing the frescoes within the lived spaces of the villa. Here, for the first time, the painted walls and mosaic floors can be seen together within an architectural setting.

As often happens in the process of conservation, the act of reconstructing the villa, too, has brought to light several "modern errors and insecure memories" and demanded a return to the earliest records, thereby correcting our inherited picture of the villa. In addition to excavation reports and newspaper articles, the early records include photographs (now in the Berlin Antikensammlung) that were made in July and October 1900, before the frescoes were removed from the walls (see figs. 11, 12, and also figs. 84, 85). Above all, no study of the villa would be possible without the invaluable documentation made by the Italian archaeologist Felice Barnabei. He produced the only extant floor plan of the villa (fig. 13) and published a detailed description of the archaeological site and its frescoes in 1901, shortly after the villa itself was reburied. Two years later sixty-eight sections of the villa's painted walls were dispersed through auction in Paris to more than eight collections in Europe and the United States. Barnabei himself was actually engaged in an act of reconstruction. In the fall of 1900 he spent weeks examining the recently detached frescoes in a crowded storeroom at the Boscoreale train station, observing the frescoes left in situ at the excavated site, and studying comparable paintings in Pompeii and at the Museo Archeologico Nazionale in Naples. This was far from the "eyewitness" account it is often assumed to be, making all the more remarkable Barnabei's ability to capture, at times in rapturous prose, the magnificent visual effects of the interior spaces of the Villa of P. Fannius Synistor.

Anyone who has attempted to convey the experience of moving through the interior of the villa has inevitably marveled at the artful marriage of painting and architecture. The recontextualization aims to evoke this experience by presenting new ways of looking at the villa and posing new questions. To date, scholars have focused on the north wing of the main floor (see fig. 37), from which the majority of the frescoes came. The frescoes, in turn, have been examined as individual panels and, in a few rare cases, as three-dimensional rooms, with attention directed primarily to the identification of the depicted buildings, objects, and figures or to the use of Euclidean perspective. The new virtual model of the Villa of P. Fannius Synistor (fig. 14) recreates a Roman domestic environment with an immediacy and accuracy that allows viewers to imagine themselves moving through the embellished rooms. Where the information was available, line drawings have been introduced to fill in the missing parts in the frescoes (see figs. 39–42, 49, 53). The effect of the frescoes within the original designs is quite different from the impression they make hanging as separate panels on the blank walls of museums.

Lehmann recognized that the illusionistic frescoes in the *cubiculum nocturnum*, or bedroom, from Boscoreale that are installed in the Metropolitan allude to the environment of a rustic villa (see figs. 55–57), but much less was understood of that environment in 1953. Today, evidence of plant, animal, and human life, all so well preserved by the eruption of Mount Vesuvius in A.D. 79, is collected in Boscoreale itself in the Antiquarium of Man and Environment in the Territory of Vesuvius, founded in 1991. New attention to the broader physical context of the frescoes shows how in planning and executing their designs the Roman architects, painters, and landscapers thought in terms of inhabited spaces that were experienced *over time*. Factors such as season, time of day, and whether a person strolled, entertained, or slept in an interior affected its decoration.

The Villa of P. Fannius Synistor was only partially excavated. It consisted of three stories and included baths, agricultural quarters, and an underground passage with a stable. The surviving evidence indicates

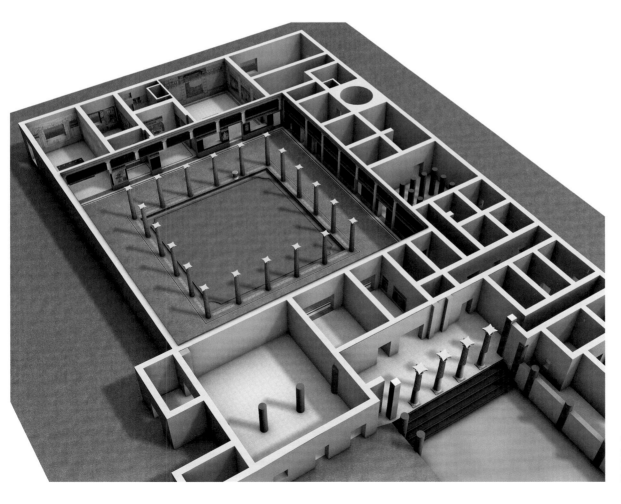

14. Virtual model of the Villa of Publius Fannius Synistor, Boscoreale

15. Fragmentary jug inscribed P[UBLIUS] FANNI SYNISTORIS S[EXTARIOS] xxxiiii inside the mouth, from the Villa of P. Fannius Synistor. Bronze; h. 15⅛ in. (38.5 cm), diam. 7⅜ in. (18.8 cm). Antiquarium, Boscoreale (16994)

that the villa was built shortly after 50 B.C. The eponymous Publius Fannius Synistor, who is named in the inscription on a fragmentary bronze vessel found near the wine press in the agricultural section of the villa (fig. 15), was in fact probably not its owner but rather the producer of wine or oil at the establishment. Lucius Herennius Florus, however, whose name appears on a stamp found in the villa's baths (fig. 16), may indeed have owned the complex at one time.[21]

The house and its outbuildings sat surrounded by orderly rows of fruit trees and vines on a country road a mile and a quarter north of Pompeii. Nearby, the famous Villa della Pisanella nestled among further vineyards and orchards. By the late first century B.C. this area, the *pagus* (district) Augustus Felix Suburbanus, must have been one of the most intensively cultivated parts of Italy. The slopes of Vesuvius are barren today, but two thousand years ago the mountainside presented an array of scenery: thick green forests grew below the summit, farther down wild animals roamed through oak and beech groves, and on the lower slopes regularly planted fields exploited the fertile volcanic soil. The economic and social life of the region took place in a

16. Stamp (top and bottom) inscribed L*HER*FLO (for Lucius Herennius Florus), from the Villa of Publius Fannius Synistor. Bronze, w. 3⅜ in. (8.7 cm). The Metropolitan Museum of Art, Fletcher Fund, 1930 (30.11.2)

network of small landholdings, or *villae rusticae*, that were either run by families or overseen by slaves. In addition to buildings housing agricultural operations, mainly wine making and olive oil production and servants' quarters, several of these villas boasted richly decorated residential quarters for the occasional visits of landlords.

When Vesuvius erupted in the fall of A.D. 79, most of the inhabitants of the Villa of P. Fannius Synistor appear to have escaped. A porter caught in the entry (Room C on the plan, fig. 13) was not so lucky, and a horse perished in the underground stable. The eruption destroyed the two upper floors of the villa,[22] which must have offered abundant light and ventilation along with sweeping views of surrounding estates, the blue waters of the Bay of Naples to the west, and the mountain ranges to the north, south, and east. The villa may have been larger than Barnabei's plan indicates. The agricultural section and the underground cryptoporticus were not fully excavated in 1899–1900, when the primary focus was the central level with its impressive Corinthian peristyle and lavish north wing housing rooms that must have accommodated the patron and his guests (see fig. 37).

Compared to nearby villas of the time, however, the Villa of P. Fannius Synistor was a compact complex with a relatively small farming operation that probably served the villa rather than producing exports for the market. The Villa della Pisanella and Villa Regina, both also in Boscoreale, boasted more extensive storage of wine and oil (see fig. 2), and the Villa of P. Fannius Synistor had no atrium, pool, or sculpture collection, as did the opulent seaside Villa dei Papiri at Herculaneum and the villa at Oplontis.[23] Yet to judge from its decor, the Villa of P. Fannius Synistor was far from modest. In addition to a fully heated bath complex and an interior garden with marble fountains, the excavations revealed that it was decorated with the highest quality Roman frescoes ever found.

Visitors entered a monumental forecourt on the south side of the villa and ascended five high steps of Vesuvian stone (A and B on the plan). At the top of the steps rose four tall "marble" columns (built of reticulate masonry and covered in white stucco to simulate stone). Frescoes between the columns on the parapet wall alongside the walkway leading to the stairs depicted illusionistic trees, birds, and metal vessels, and garden frescoes also embellished the front wall of the villa, so that the exterior facade must have seemed to disappear into the natural plantings. Upon reaching the top step, an attentive visitor might have noted an inscription carved into the column just to the left recording that on May 9, A.D. 12, an auction had taken place, but whether this marked the public sale of a household slave, a beast of burden, or perhaps the villa itself is not known. In the west corner of the airy entry space (B), visitors could pay respects at the household shrine (*lararium*). It must have contained miniature statues of the domestic gods, which had apparently already been removed in antiquity.

From the entrance visitors entered Room C, the *fauces* ("jaws") of the house (figs. 17, 18), where the walls were painted to emulate white marble columns and thin slabs of imported precious stones, a new fashion that according to Pliny was introduced in Rome in the first century B.C. (*Natural History* 36.48–50).²⁴ From this entrance hall the light-filled heart of the villa came into view. The effect must have been spectacular. Majestic Corinthian columns supported a glittering ceiling that imitated ivory and gold leaf (so-called chryselephantine work).

17. Fragment of a fresco from the east wall of Room C of the Villa of P. Fannius Synistor. 5 ft. 8½ in. x 5 ft. 7 in. (1.74 x 1.7 m). Musée du Louvre, Paris (P102 [MND616])

18. Virtual model of the Villa of P. Fannius Synistor, looking north from inside Room C to the peristyle (E). The fresco fragments on the right wall are in the Musée du Louvre, Paris (P101 [MND615] and see fig. 17).

20. Corinthian column with leaves, wheat, and pomegranates. Fragment of a fresco from the east end of the south wall of the peristyle (E) of the Villa of P. Fannius Synistor. 35¾ x 25½ in. (90.8 x 64.8 cm). The Metropolitan Museum of Art, Rogers Fund, 1903 (03.14.1)

19. Virtual model of the Villa of P. Fannius Synistor, looking north across the peristyle (E). No attempt has been made in the model to re-create either the plants that would have filled the peristyle or the marble fountains.

Underfoot, the pavement sparkled with tiny pieces of colorful stone. At the corners of the open space planted with hedges, bushes, and flowers, marble fountains spurted jets of water.

This was a place for movement, and the decor provided a rhythmic succession of prospects for the viewer. One of the most rewarding aspects of walking through a villa, Roman writers said, was the variety of views enjoyed during the customary *ambulatio*. Leafy or marine vistas framed by columns were coveted benefits of *otium*, that state of leisure, ease, and repose that combined physical pleasure and intellectual stimulation.[25] In the late first century B.C. the architect Vitruvius emphasized that attention should be paid to the experience of space, specifically through optical refinements of *eurythmia*, namely rhythm, direction, and structure (*On Architecture* 7.5.2). Through the harmonious arrangement of the individual parts of a building, a beautiful impression (*venustas species*) and a proper appearance (*commodus aspectus*) in turn engender pleasure of the senses (*voluptas*). In the Villa of P. Fannius Synistor, axiality and symmetry coordinated the real with the simulated, the rational with the imaginative, to render views with appealing associations.[26]

Imagine strolling along the colonnades of the peristyle (fig. 19). Painted simulations expanded the space. On the walls, twenty-two fictive Corinthian columns replicated their built counterparts. The fragment that survives from the south wall (fig. 20) exemplifies the way that painters juxtaposed nature and the man-made. Green leaves, a sheaf of golden grain, and a cluster of reddish pomegranates materialize from behind the sculpted white acanthus leaves of a marble Corinthian capital. While the painted columns mirrored the actual columns standing in front of them, the golden wheat complemented the gilded rosettes glinting in the ceiling immediately above. Between the painted capitals of the twenty-two columns swung copious garlands laden with ripe fruits. At first glance, the steady sequence of vertical columns and horizontal garlands creates an impression of sameness. For the person who stopped to examine details, however, that uniformity quickly unraveled. This is best observed along the west wall, which unlike the other three sides of the peristyle lacked any door openings to interrupt the continuous design (fig. 21). Although painted high on the wall, each garland displayed a unique combination of branches, leaves, fruits, and flowers (see figs. 22,

23). Using varying brushstrokes and multihued pigments, the painters captured nuances of specific shapes and textures: white lilies with delicate petals, eye-catching red oleander blossoms, large vine shoots and shiny little globes of yellowish grapes, green and brown pinecones, all accurately depicted and gathered together in silver rings at the midpoint of each garland.[27] One wonders if on certain days in October the yield of the autumn harvest hung in fresh festoons between the real columns of the peristyle, swaying gently in the breeze and emitting sweet scents.

21. Virtual model of the Villa of P. Fannius Synistor, looking north along the west side of the peristyle (E). The three fresco panels at the top left are in the Villa Kérylos (see fig. 23). The floors would have been white with colorful pieces of stone.

22. Corinthian column and garland. Fragment of a fresco from the south end of the west wall of the peristyle (E) of the Villa of P. Fannius Synistor. 44½ x 106¼ in. (113 x 270 cm). Museo Archeologico Nazionale di Napoli (s.n. 2)

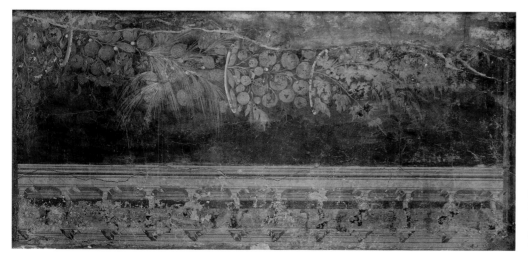

23. Garland and frieze with centaurs. Fragment of a fresco from the west wall of the peristyle (E) of the Villa of P. Fannius Synistor. 48⅞ x 96⅞ in. (124 x 246 cm). Villa Kérylos, Beaulieu-sur-Mer, France

A podium imitating yellow marble from North Africa (*giallo antico*) ran around the lower walls of the peristyle. On it was displayed an array of luxury vessels in gold, silver, copper, and bronze (see fig. 24), as well as marble basins and statues and even the hat and mantle of the god Mercury. The emphatic materialism attests the fashion during the Late Republic for collecting and also for commissioning

24. Vase (calyx krater) on a marble block with palm fronds behind. Fragment of a fresco from the west end of the north wall of the peristyle (E) of the Villa of P. Fannius Synistor. 58 x 46 in. (147.3 x 116.8 cm). The Metropolitan Museum of Art, Rogers Fund, 1903 (03.14.3). The original jet black background has faded.

25. Virtual model of the Villa of P. Fannius Synistor, southwest corner of the peristyle (E). For the fresco fragments, see figs. 22, 26, 27. The fragment with the garland at the far right is in the Villa Kérylos, Beaulieu-sur-Mer, France.

26–27. Fresco fragments from the west end of the south wall of the peristyle (E) of the Villa of P. Fannius Synistor. Left: marble table with athletic prizes. 48⅜ x 87⅜ in. (123 x 222 cm). Museo Archeologico Nazionale di Napoli (s.n. 6). Right: globe with a gnomon on top. 28⅜ x 19⅝ in. (72.1 x 49.8 cm). The Metropolitan Museum of Art, Rogers Fund, 1903 (03.14.2)

reproductions of exotic objects, both natural and man-made.[28] Set against a burnished black surface, these vivid objects simultaneously receded and threw back reflections. In the southwest corner of the peristyle (fig. 25), two large (painted) marble tables exhibited athletic prizes of a palm branch, victors' ribbons, and trophies (fig. 26). On a nearby wall a painted globe rendered with a gnomon on top

and latitudes and longitudes along its sides (fig. 27) faced an actual, functioning marble sundial standing in the garden. (Examples of this novel state-of-the-art timekeeping device were found in a few other elegant Campanian villas; the current whereabouts of the sundial and the marble fountains removed from the Villa of P. Fannius Synistor are unknown.)[29] As sunlight shifted between the columns,

28. Virtual model of the Villa of P. Fannius Synistor, north side of the peristyle (E). For the fresco fragments, see figs. 24, 34, 35.

the play of shadow and reflection on the polished black walls must have blurred the difference between real and painted objects. What is more, the painted surfaces were so highly reflective of any light thrown upon them that viewers could never lose sight of themselves within the visual field.

From floor to ceiling the peristyle walls offered an infinite variety of animal, mineral, and vegetable forms. The lifelike movement did not end with the garlands but continued to the supposedly static architectural features in the frieze directly below, where agitated centaurs reared up on their hind legs, pawing the air to present a sacrificial dish or to brandish a staff. These white modillions (ornamental brackets typically found beneath a cornice in the Corinthian order) project forward, casting shadows onto a purple frieze. Such animated details recur again and again in the fictive architecture of the Villa of P. Fannius Synistor.

On the north wall, however, the carefully crafted illusions of the peristyle were challenged by a series of wide doorways (fig. 28, and see figs. 19, 21). Column shafts suddenly terminated, exposing views through rooms into the real landscape beyond. Such contradictions might seem jarring to present-day

viewers, but ancient Romans clearly enjoyed visual paradoxes. As Phyllis Lehmann explained, the ancient spectator "preferred to ignore those structural openings registered by his eyes and to maintain his intellectual concept. Decoratively speaking, those openings had ceased to exist for him. This cardinal point cannot be overemphasized to the modern spectator for whom this alien attitude constitutes a barrier to understanding, let alone enjoyment, that is seldom overcome. Yet, overcome it must be, if one is really to see this house."[30]

The peristyle was the heart of the dwelling that opened onto discrete spheres. Visitors entered through the impressive forecourt (A and B) and *fauces* (C) to circulate around the spacious peristyle (E), finally stopping at one of the northern reception rooms (N, M, H, G). Other persons such as workers, servants, or messengers probably followed alternate routes through small doors in the entry

29. City wall with a gate and two towers. Fragment of a mosaic from the small peristyle (15) in the Villa of P. Fannius Synistor. W. 40⅛ in. (102 cm). Musée Royal de Mariemont, Morlanwelz, Belgium (Nr. B 100)

30. Virtual model of the Villa of P. Fannius Synistor, the exedra (L), looking north. The fresco fragment on the back wall is in the Musée Royal de Mariemont, Morlanwelz, Belgium (R61); the two fragments on the right are in the Musée de Picardie, Amiens (see fig. 32). For the left wall, see fig. 31.

31. Garland with a bull's head, a snake emerging from a basket, and a Silenus mask. Fragment of a fresco from the west wall of Room L of the Villa of P. Fannius Synistor. 77 x 107 in. (195.6 x 271.8 cm). The Metropolitan Museum of Art, Rogers Fund, 1903 (03.14.4). This image shows the fresco with the modern restoration of the upper left corner in place.

space into the *pars rustica* (24), to a stairway leading upstairs (1), or to the steps down into the cryptoporticus (12). Servants could come and go from the outside through this underground area, which housed a horse stall and the hypocaust system that heated the entire wing. The objects found in the rooms (now dispersed) add to our knowledge of life in the villa.[31] The kitchen areas of the eastern wing (13, 14) were outfitted with a grain mill, an oven, a stove, frying pans, and many other utilitarian items. In the small peristyle in this section of the villa (15), near the latrine (11), was a black and white floor mosaic depicting a city wall with gates and crenellated towers (fig. 29). Toward the north end of the east wing was a complete set of baths offering hot and cold water (18–22), where a gold ring and the brick stamp naming the possible owner Lucius Herennius Florus (see fig. 16) were found. In the agricultural area, a wine press (*torcularium*), olive press (*trapetum*), and farming tools indicated active production. The functional objects could be quite ornate: one bronze container had a decorative appliqué in the form of Bacchus, god of wine, covered with silver leaves. Another bronze vessel, used as a measuring cup, bears the inscription on its lip stating its capacity as thirteen liters and naming the producer, P. Fannius Synistor, from whom the villa received its modern name (see fig. 15).

The quarters surrounding the peristyle thus housed a range of activities, with the areas devoted to the labor needed to sustain a farm and a home effectively masked by the visual unity and symmetry of the decor. An example of the carefully balanced layout can be seen in the so-called Room of Musical Instruments (D), on the south end of the house, and the exedra (L), a recess or niche on the north, which faced each other directly across the open garden space. Both rooms were laid with white floor mosaics, and the low-lying garlands painted on their walls echoed the visual rise and fall of festoons in the peristyle. The garlands and their accessories in the two rooms "spoke to each other," celebrating Bacchus with flora and objects specific to his cult. Near the center of each wall in the exedra, the fresco depicted a bull's head nailed to lavish red sheathing (see figs. 30, 31). The animal looks amazingly alive and quite unlike the traditional, skinned oxen skulls (*bucrania*) commemorating sacrifices at ancient

shrines. The hole in the forehead and the slightly open eyes suggest that it has just been decapitated for sacrifice. A string of pearls is wrapped around the horns, and the heavy swags tied to the ears fall in long arcs across the walls, their thick clusters of grapes, pinecones, acorns, poppies, and oak leaves turning in the shifting light. The vegetation adds a temporary dimension that together with the ambient light produces the illusion of a moment, as the sun strikes objects, casting shadows and situating the viewer in an alternate reality. On the fresco fragment from the back (north) wall (see fig. 30), a satyr mask with startling eyes and gaping mouth presents an arresting contrast to the bull's head above. To the left a dead hare dangles beside heavy golden grapes, and a little farther on a shiny bronze cymbalum connects to illuminated brown pinecones above. And so it goes around the room. Below the bull's head on the left (west) wall (fig. 31) a snake with open eyes and jaws slithers from a *cista mystica*, a basket used in Bacchic initiation ceremonies. To the right of that, a laughing Silenus mask and a cymbalum catch the eye. On the opposite (east) wall a tympanum and cymbalum (fig. 32) evoke the music of Bacchic revelry.

32. Garland with a tympanum and a cymbalum. Fragment of a fresco from the left side of the east wall of Room L of the Villa of P. Fannius Synistor. 72⅞ x 43¼ in. (185 x 110 cm). Musée de Picardie, Amiens

33. Garland and crossed flutes. Fragment of a fresco from Room D of the Villa of P. Fannius Synistor. 49¼ x 46½ in. (125 x 118 cm). Musée du Louvre, Paris (P100 [MND614])

34–35. Winged guardian figures. Fragments of frescoes from the north wall of the peristyle (E) of the Villa of P. Fannius Synistor. H. of each 49⅝ in. (126 cm). Left: Musée du Louvre, Paris (P23 [MND613]; see also inside back cover); right: Allard Pierson Museum, Amsterdam

As if in dialogue, Room D, across the courtyard, also presented colorful simulations of inlaid stones, but assembled to different effect, with yellow ocher predominating over cinnabar red. Swags of wispy green pine needles and bulbous pinecones swung across a light yellow background; lifesize musical instruments—pairs of flutes (fig. 33) and (now lost) cymbals, castanets, a trumpet, and a syrinx—dangled at eye level. Here, as elsewhere in the villa, objects awaited their agents, in this case Bacchus's satyrs and maenads, to initiate the festivities by picking up the instruments, playing the god's rousing tunes, and spinning around the peristyle. The moment is anticipatory.

Indeed, an otherworldly theme permeated the optically enhanced spaces of the Villa of P. Fannius Synistor. Nowhere is this more evident than at three separate entries to the peristyle, where a person moving around the colonnades would have encountered pairs of lifesize, half-human creatures guarding doors: at the *fauces* (C), at a small door in the southwest corner, and at the entry to the magnificent Room H on the north side. Only one of the pairs survives: the winged male and female who rose from the yellow podium on either side of the door from the peristyle into H (figs. 34, 35). With their inclined postures and alert gazes, the hybrid creatures stand at attention, challenging the entrant to make eye contact while proffering an object in an extended hand, she a dish of fruit, he a sacrificial dish (*patera*). Seen first from the forecourt through the entry and then again from countless points within the peristyle (fig. 36, and see also figs. 19, 28), the custodians drew attention to the majestic figure they framed, namely, the goddess Venus painted on the back wall of Room H. Visibility was paramount in the design of this central room, which could be seen through the door and also through the two large picture windows that were exactly the width of the space between the columns before them. Walking through the peristyle, viewers could glimpse shifting groups of figures—some human, others divine—turning and gesturing against vivid red walls. The rooms are inhabited, and not just by us.

The spell intensified inside the rooms for reception, entertaining, and relaxation in the north wing (fig. 37). Entering the spacious square hall (H) for the first time must have stunned visitors, who

36. Virtual model of the Villa of P. Fannius Synistor, entrance to Room H on the north wall of the peristyle (E). For the fresco fragments, see figs. 34, 35, 38–41, 44–46.

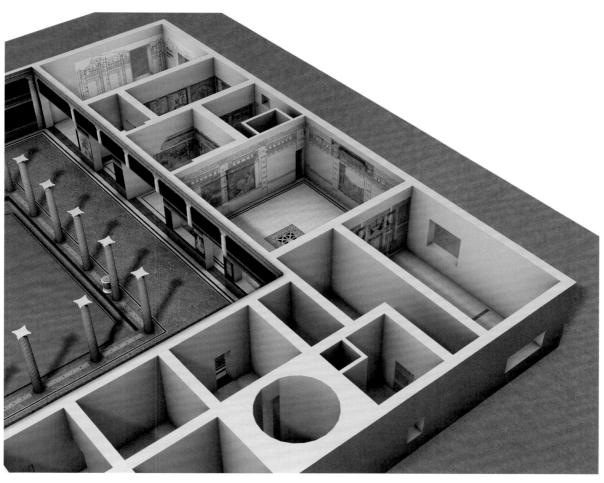

37. Virtual model of the Villa of P. Fannius Synistor, north wing, looking northwest

38. Venus. Fragment of a fresco from the north wall of Room H of the Villa of P. Fannius Synistor. 74 x 74 in. (188 x 188 cm). Museo Archeologico Nazionale di Napoli (s.n. 4)

39. Virtual model of the Villa of P. Fannius Synistor, Room H, looking north. For the fresco fragments, see figs. 38, 41, 44–46.

yellow and purple (fig. 38) was without doubt the focal point of the room. On her raised thigh the goddess balances a kneeling Eros who lifts his arm to hurl a dart, probably at Psyche, who stands before a round temple on the seashore in the right background. The two erotes beside Psyche are fishing. On the opposite shore the porch of another monumental building displays two female statues, one of them Fortuna with her horn of plenty. The rich dedications of the sanctuary testify to Venus's marine origins and to the ongoing worship of her.

Originally the picture of Venus was one of three scenes on the back wall, each set against an azure sky (fig. 39). Together, they presented a resplendent triad of divine beauty: on the left a languorous Bacchus, god of pleasure (who often joins Venus in Roman pictorial ensembles), reclined in the lap of a female companion, and on the right the Three Graces, Venus's frequent companions and the embodiment of her beauty, posed arm in arm in their customary embrace.[32] Against these cool, pastel scenes the brilliant cinnabar red walls to the east and west posed a dramatic contrast that signaled the human sphere. (A similar contrast of red walls and blue vista is found in the Villa dei Misteri, where the room with the *megalographia*, a large-scale painting depicting lifesize figures like these, opened onto a view of the

suddenly found themselves sharing space with lifesize illusions of living, breathing figures. Painted Corinthian columns continued the actual architecture of the peristyle, so that Venus appeared to step into the room. The statuesque, frontal figure in bright

40. Virtual model of the Villa of P. Fannius Synistor, Room H, looking west. The fresco panel on the far wall is from the Museo Archeologico Nazionale di Napoli (s.n. 5); for the fragment on the right wall, see fig. 44. When the eruption came in A.D. 79, the north end of the west wall was white and evidently still unpainted, possibly a sign of a renovation following damage from the earthquake of A.D. 62.

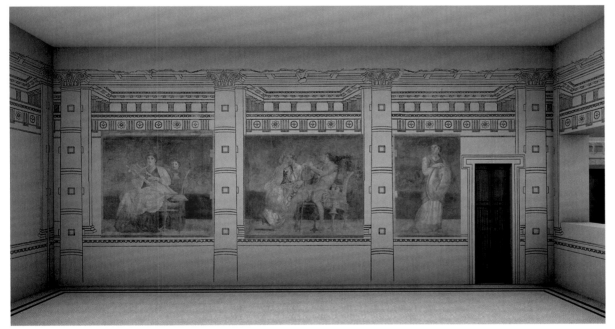

41. Virtual model of the Villa of P. Fannius Synistor, Room H, looking east. The three fresco panels are in The Metropolitan Museum of Art (Rogers Fund, 1903 [03.14.5–7]); for a detail of the center scene, see cover illustration.

Bay of Naples.)[33] The large figures sit, stand, and look about as if hearing or seeing something. A few might be portraits of rulers of the Hellenistic East, but their identification continues to challenge scholars.[34] On the fresco from the west wall (fig. 40) a hunched older man, maybe a philosopher, leans on his crook and stares at a pair of elaborately attired women who seem to be engaged in conversation or a moment of mutual reflection. In the scene from the left end of the east wall (fig. 41), a seated woman in beautifully rendered white and purple garments strums a golden cithara as she and the young girl standing behind her chair look toward the entrance. In the central scene a stately, intent couple share a throne. Like their counterparts across the room they are lost either in conversation or reflection: the elaborately draped woman leans forward, legs crossed and chin on fist in a meditative pose, gazing at (or past?) the nude male, who sits back, his crossed hands resting on a golden staff. The young female

42. Virtual model of the Villa of P. Fannius Synistor, south wall of Room H. For the fresco fragment above the door, see fig. 43; for the panel on the right (west) wall, see fig. 40. The fragment of a painted column to the right of the door is in The Metropolitan Museum of Art (Gift of C. & E. Canessa, 1908 [08.264]).

who stands facing the entrance on the right end of the wall turns her head to look back and up toward the ceiling above Venus. With her right hand she props a polished shield on her knees, and the nude youth reflected in the shield's convex surface also looks to the left, leading the viewer's eye again toward the north. The painted architectural details continued onto the south wall of H (fig. 42), framing the two large windows and the door that gave onto the peristyle, above which a grimacing, wide-eyed mask of the goat god Pan (fig. 43) formed part of the frieze that encircled the room.

43. Mask of Pan. Fragment of a fresco from the south wall of Room H of the Villa of P. Fannius Synistor. 16⅞ x 22½ in. (43 x 57 cm). Musée Bonnat, Bayonne (604)

The *megalographia* in Room H seems to have been not a narrative sequence but rather a series of scenes happening all at once. Figures gaze across the room, involved in a dynamic web of interaction, but the nature of that interaction remains elusive. Instinctively the eye tends to the center of an image, to things at eye level, and to the human form. In Roman rooms, however, viewers are rewarded by attending to apparently marginal details. In the upper zone of the north wall were three small pictures with wooden shutters (*pinakes*) propped on a golden cornice, each directly above a divine scene (figs. 44–46, and see fig. 39). This fascinating trio offers one key to the artful cross-referencing within the room's design. The *pinax* from above the reclining Bacchus depicts a seated female and an attendant with a shield between them, a miniature version of the central couple on the adjacent west wall, while the picture from above the Three Graces varies that grouping, with the woman sitting on a rock, a young male beside her, and an altar on the left. In the central panel of the upper register, directly above Venus, the shutters open to reveal a single female figure echoing the goddess below. The independent pictures thus corresponded to the "real" lifesize figures below. Visual links between the walls created by the echoing compositions and the gazes of the figures

are fully realized in the fictive illumination of the room, for a unifying shaft of light projects from overhead toward the entrance, introducing a permanent light source competing with the daylight filtering through that entrance. Transience is captured in a two-dimensional medium and remains frozen in place.

In the north wing the larger spaces for entertainment (H, N, and G) connected with smaller, more intimate rooms, forming three distinct suites. Within the suites lay hidden spaces (F and I) with their own windows and soothing, richly surfaced interiors (figs. 47–49). The designs of the larger rooms offered variations on the paintings of the peristyle. The east and west walls were apparent mirror images of each other, while the north wall, opposite the entrance, presented an ethereal outdoor view of grottoes and distant landscapes.

Both the builder and the painters exploited the orientation of rooms for light, air, and framed views onto fertile fields and the commanding mountain. Only the central hall, Room H, was closed to the outdoors on the north, instead receiving light through the columns of the peristyle and the large windows on the south that looked into the peristyle. In place of a window, the goddess Venus stepped from a cerulean seascape on the north wall—an arresting vision for someone walking by and expecting another real prospect through a window. The large corner rooms (N and G) made the most of their exposure, with two windows opening to the north and west and to the north and east, respectively. In both rooms, the viewer encountered successive layers of architectural illusion and contradictory visual cues.

The dining room (G) exemplified the purposeful confusion of the real and the simulated in four distinct and simultaneous prospects, two of them painted vistas and two actual views through the windows (see fig. 50).[35] The left section of the west wall (fig. 51), once illuminated by large windows on the north and east, captures essential aspects of the frescoes throughout the villa. The viewer's eye instantly meets the transfixed stare and gaping mouth of a tragic mask set upon a golden cornice. At first glance,

44–46. Fragments of a fresco from the north wall of Room H of the Villa of P. Fannius Synistor (see fig. 39). Top left and right: 16¾ x 16½ in. (42.5 x 41.9 cm), 17¼ x 17¼ in. (43.8 x 43.8 cm); The Metropolitan Museum of Art, Rogers Fund, 1903 (03.14.9, 8). Below: 41¾ x 130¾ in. (106 x 332 cm); Museo Archeologico Nazionale di Napoli (s.n. 3)

the green background appears to recede. On a second look, it is not airy distance but inlaid blocks of green marble on a solid wall, a Roman painter's typical play of color, space, and surface. Below, gold architectural elements project from a bright cinnabar wall. The white marble telamones and caryatids appear alive: each in a different pose, they gesture, stand, and run. From the top right edge of the adjacent wall three remarkable heads incorporated into the capitals of the Corinthian columns peer down on the viewer (fig. 52). The optical game begins again.

At the western end of the villa, Room N was painted with the familiar Corinthian colonnade, and red and yellow partition walls rose from a black podium to open into an imaginary precinct crowded with rows of large and small Doric columns. Crowning the red partition wall on either side of the large window on the north wall was a brilliant red monochrome frieze populated with temples and figures at shrines that stood above a purple frieze depicting Nereids, Tritons, erotes, and sea monsters (figs. 53, 54).[36]

Each room created an entirely different experience. The cubiculum, or bedroom (M), recently reinstalled in the Metropolitan Museum (see fig. 80 and also fig. 98), offers a rare opportunity to occupy a relatively complete interior from the villa. The room was divided into an antechamber (O), a central space, and a vaulted area for a couch. At first sight the east and west walls seem to be identical, but again, closer observation reveals them to be analogues rather than exact duplicates (figs. 55, 56).[37] Statues, buildings, masks, and endless other details

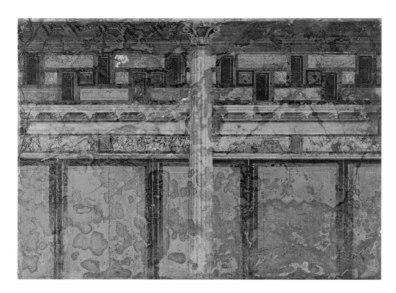

47. Virtual model of the Villa of P. Fannius Synistor, Room F, looking east. The three fresco fragments are in The Metropolitan Museum of Art (Rogers Fund, 1903 [03.14.10–12]).

48. Fresco panel from the west wall of Room I of the Villa of P. Fannius Synistor. 6 ft. 11½ in. x 10 ft. 3¼ in. (2.12 x 3.13 m). Musées Royaux d'Art et d'Histoire, Brussels

49. Virtual model of the Villa of P. Fannius Synistor, Room I, looking north. The fresco fragment on the back wall (along with another, similar fragment from the south wall) is in the Musée Royal de Mariemont, Morlanwelz, Belgium (R58); for the panel on the left wall, see fig. 48.

50. Virtual model of the Villa of P. Fannius Synistor, Room G, looking southwest. The fresco fragment on the south (left) wall is in the Musée Royal de Mariemont, Morlanwelz, Belgium (R56; see also fig. 52); the three fragments on the west (right) wall are in the Museo Archeologico Nazionale di Napoli (s.n. 1; see also fig. 51).

52. Three column capitals with human heads. Detail of a fresco fragment from the south wall of Room G of the Villa of P. Fannius Synistor (see fig. 50)

51. Fresco panel from the west wall of Room G of the Villa of P. Fannius Synistor. 11 ft. ⅝ in. x 3 ft. 11¼ in. (3.37 x 1.2 m). Museo Archeologico Nazionale di Napoli (see fig. 50 and back cover)

show the immense variety to be found within the scenes. For someone standing in the room, the overall framework of a podium, Corinthian columns, and a cornice creates a coherent space, yet relations between nearby objects and distant structures challenge the putative boundaries between inside and outside. Masks and ritual offerings operate as "shifters," transition points between realms. This is clearest on the north wall (fig. 57), where on either side of the window is an outdoor scene with a grotto, a hill, and a trellised arbor supporting clusters of ripe

purple grapes. With the wooden shutters open, the scenes either contrasted with or continued views of the real landscape outside. The window seems to sever the top of a yellow panel that recalls materials such as parchment, marble, or metal; on its ambiguous surface emerges a mirage of bridges, colonnades, towers, and fishermen, another alternative to the landscape offered through the window.[38] Outside

54. Fragment of a fresco from the north wall of Room N of the Villa of P. Fannius Synistor. 31⅛ x 28⅜ in. (79 x 72 cm). Musée Royal de Mariemont, Morlanwelz, Belgium (R60)

and inside, reality and simulation vied for attention. Indeed, the frescoes in this small room exhibit an entire range of materials derived from nature: wood, gold, silver, ivory, marble, glass, ripe fruit, along with the virtuoso human craftsmanship that shaped them.

One of the continuing puzzles of Boscoreale is the fact that some of the painted simulations seem to prefigure the existence of actual architecture and artifacts. Just to the right of the window on the north wall of the cubiculum is a bowl filled with peaches, quinces, green almonds, and twigs (fig. 58), all visible thanks to the technology of transparent blown glass, which had not yet been introduced in Italy. The detail recalls the observation Seneca made in A.D. 65, decades after these frescoes were painted, that "fruits are much larger when seen through a glass" (*Naturales quaestiones* 1.3.9).

The luxury of detail can only be appreciated over time. Again and again, lines converge in a sacred edifice, leading us to the image of a goddess. Everywhere one looks there are signs of worship and sacrifice in progress: glowing coals for burning incense on altars, columns bearing statues of Diana-Hecate and wrapped with yellow ribbons, sacred portals strung with garlands, "Adonis gardens," broken terracotta

pots planted with lettuce and fennel, ribbons and fruit left as offerings at thresholds. Miniature friezes over painted doors depict women partaking in religious ceremonies. Parading along the tops of gates and walls is a continuous row of phalluses.[39] In the painters' art of repetition and echoing, the same things appear at varying scales and in different planes of reality. The subject of the decor is the moment, and it is a moment of celebration. Upon exiting this space, a visitor passed through painted walls framing the door to the peristyle (figs. 59, 60) that offered a contrast to these spatial illusions; the solid walls of purple, red, green, and yellow stonework each display a vertical arrangement of an elegant metal amphora and a suspended garland with ribbons, ritual signs seen elsewhere in the room.

In the villa, distinctions among sacred, urban, and domestic spheres were obscured. The rich

55–56. Fresco panels from the west and east walls of the cubiculum, or bedroom (M), of the Villa of P. Fannius Synistor. W. of each 19 ft. (5.79 m). The Metropolitan Museum of Art, Rogers Fund, 1903 (03.14.13a–g)

57 (above left). Fresco from the north wall of the cubiculum (M) of the Villa of P. Fannius Synistor. W. 10 ft. 10 in. (3.3 m). The Metropolitan Museum of Art, Rogers Fund, 1903 (03.14.13a–g)

59–60 (above right). Fresco panels from either side of the doorway on the south wall of the cubiculum (M) of the Villa of P. Fannius Synistor. H. of each 9 ft. ¼ in. (2.75 m). The Metropolitan Museum of Art, Rogers Fund, 1903 (03.14.13a–g)

vocabulary of architecture and objects transported the viewer into a magical world, where bejeweled red columns wound with golden tendrils emerge from calyxes of gilded acanthus leaves. Such forms had decorated the festive constructions of Hellenistic kings, but more immediate parallels are found in dwellings in Italy of the late first century B.C.[40] Similarly bejeweled monoliths, for example, adorned the contemporary villa at Oplontis. In the cubiculum from Boscoreale the metallic vines wind around the column right beside the "real" vines growing wild over the rocky grotto. But look closer: even the

grotto is artifice, for the marble basin is fed by a jet whose plumbing travels back under the hill.[41]

The frescoes in the villa were never painted over and may have been on view for more than a century. What would it have been like for a person to see these walls every day over a period of months, years, decades? These paintings speak to us today because they are about experience and perception, and just as Roman inhabitants did, we can place ourselves within their finely crafted illusions. With exposure over time, the painted interior promotes different modes of seeing and of being in space, in this case a space also inhabited by gods.

More than a century ago, Felice Barnabei captured his own experience of the frescoes from the Villa of P. Fannius Synistor in exalted prose. Fifty years later, Phyllis Lehmann added learned insights to the picture. This visualization of the frescoes in their architectural context offers a fresh view and invites future exploration of a lost, now reimagined, Roman villa.

58. Detail of fig. 57

The Conservation of the Frescoes from Boscoreale in the Metropolitan Museum

RUDOLF MEYER

The frescoes from the Villa of Publius Fannius Synistor at Boscoreale are beautiful examples of superb craftsmanship and technical perfection in Roman wall painting. They were executed in the *buon fresco*, or "true" fresco, technique by painting the colors onto a freshly applied damp plaster ground. The liquid lime in the plaster (calcium hydroxide) combines with the paint and in the process of drying turns into carbonate of lime, which is chemically the same as limestone or marble. The pigments fuse permanently with the plaster, and the painting becomes remarkably durable.

Roman frescoes of good quality like those from Boscoreale typically have a perfectly smooth and shiny surface. This important feature is lacking in frescoes of later periods. At least three or four layers of plaster were necessary to achieve the desired result. In the first century B.C. the Roman architect Vitruvius described the process of applying and polishing up to seven layers of plaster with trowels and floats similar to modern-day tools. The lowest layers consisted of sand mortar, followed by plaster containing marble or alabaster dust to enhance the luster of the painting. The surface had to be impeccable before the paint was applied. After the painting was completed the fresco was burnished again, which forced lime solution to the surface and sealed the painting with a protective film. The polishing tool was a floatlike instrument called a *liaculum*. A plasterer using such a tool was depicted in a painting in Pompeii that is now lost (see fig. 61).

A telltale sign of *buon fresco* is evidence that a wall was divided into sections that could be plastered and then painted while the plaster was still damp, all in a *giornata di lavoro* (day's work), so to speak. How long the plaster stayed damp enough to paint a *buon fresco* is not known, however, and could

have been more than a day. Slightly protruding edges or cracks often betray the seams between these so-called *giornate di lavoro*, which were applied starting at the top of the wall. To render the seams less conspicuous, the edges of the sections were usually carefully placed along straight lines in the decorative scheme, as they were in the cubiculum, or bedroom, from Boscoreale that is installed at the Museum (see fig. 62).

A painter began the decoration of a wall by tracing the design onto it. His tools included a plumb bob, rulers, and compasses. Long continuous lines were plotted with string that might have been colored with chalk or charcoal or impressed into the damp plaster, as in the dado of the window wall in the Boscoreale cubiculum (the wall is panel D on the diagram in fig. 63, and see fig. 64). The two

61. Plasterer polishing a wall with a *liaculum*, after a painting (now lost) found at Pompeii in Regio IX, building 5, room 9

62. *Giornate di lavoro* ("days of work") on the west, north, and east walls of the cubiculum (Room M) from the Villa of Publius Fannius Synistor, Boscoreale (see figs. 13, 14, 55–57, 80, 98). So that the frescoes could be painted while the plaster was still damp, the walls were worked on in sections (indicated here with black outlines).

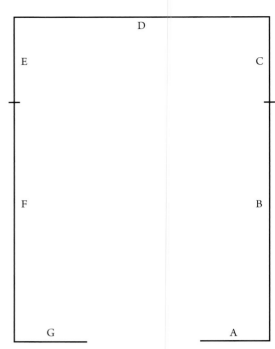

63. Diagram of the fresco panels removed from the cubiculum in the villa and reinstalled in the Metropolitan Museum. The room measured 19 ft. x 10 ft. 10 in. (5.79 x 3.3 m). The height of the frescoes up to the molding was originally 9 ft. 2¼ in. (2.8 m). It is now 9 ft. ¼ in. (2.75 m). The walls themselves were much higher.

Macedonian shields in panels B and F are outlined with the incisions of a compass (fig. 65, and see also fig. 76). Pointed tools were used to incise guide lines in the plaster, and preparatory markings with paint are also quite common (figs. 66, 67). On the whole the Boscoreale frescoes in the Metropolitan reveal remarkably scant traces of such preparation, however. No clue could be found, for instance, as to how the same townscape was rendered four times onto the walls of the cubiculum (see figs. 55, 56).

The general dimensions of all four compositions are identical, although two of them are mirror images and the architectural details vary greatly.

The colors available to a Roman painter consisted mostly of naturally occurring earth pigments like red and yellow ochers, green earth, and calcium carbonate (chalk). Black was produced from soot or charcoal. The blue was Egyptian blue (named for its land of origin), which is artificial and consists of ground blue glass frit. Bright red cinnabar, a natural pigment consisting of toxic mercuric sulfide, played a special role. Its rarity made it so costly that only wealthy patrons could afford to pay for it. Cinnabar was used profusely in the Boscoreale frescoes. Even panels from the small, modest Room F contain sizable areas painted with cinnabar (see fig. 47), and cinnabar was applied as a ground layer, followed by a white wash, on the large pink panels in Room L, the exedra (see figs. 30–32). Pigments were mixed to obtain the numerous shades necessary for the details in the decoration. Additional pigments known to the Romans, such as azurite, malachite, and lead white, were not detected in the Metropolitan's frescoes,

64. Long horizontal line marked by the impression of a string (cubiculum, panel D)

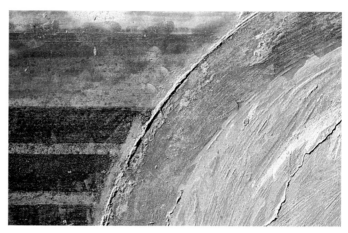

65. Macedonian shield on which the outline was incised with a compass (cubiculum, panel B)

66. Egg-and-dart frieze on which the outlines were incised with a pointed instrument (cubiculum, panel G)

67. Outline of an alcove window marked by painted line (cubiculum, panel B, left townscape)

and neither were organic dyes such as indigo, red madder, oak gall, and the fabled true purple.

The decoration of a Roman house required teams of plasterers and painters working side by side. The cubiculum was undoubtedly the product of a succession of painters, one or more of whom laid the ground with others adding details. All the bushes and trees were certainly painted by the same person (see fig. 68). The many small figures on the friezes and altars and in the yellow landscape (see figs. 69–72) can be attributed to another painter. It was not customary for Roman craftsmen to sign or initial their work, and no signatures were found on the Metropolitan's Boscoreale paintings.

Roman wall paintings in villas situated near Mount Vesuvius show much ancient intervention after a strong earthquake that occurred in A.D. 62. The event may have required the repair of an area about a foot wide and five and a half feet long along the bottom of panel B in the cubiculum. The area was restored in the fresco technique to match the older painting but remains clearly discernible (fig. 73). There are countless cracks of varying sizes, and one can assume that an earthquake caused the long continuous cracks as well as the opening of seams between the *giornate* (fig. 74).

Most of the panels from the Villa of P. Fannius Synistor came from the centers of walls and therefore show few signs of daily wear and tear. By contrast, the walls preserved in the cubiculum reveal considerable abrasion in the dado sections, especially in panels B and D. This is not surprising

68. Detail of panel B in the cubiculum (see also fig. 56). All the bushes and trees in the frescoes in the cubiculum were painted by the same artist.

considering that the villa was occupied for well over a hundred years. The eruption of Vesuvius in A.D. 79 caused extensive damage but also conserved the remaining paintings until their discovery in 1900. The eruption occurred in two phases. During the first, or Plinian, phase, ash and pumice fell for eighteen hours, burying the area in a layer of coarse dust that was as much as 9 feet deep in Pompeii. This ash rain also contained stones up to 4½ inches in diameter, which could explain numerous scratches in upper areas of walls. The evidence in the cubiculum occurs mostly on panels B and F (see fig. 75). It seems that after a ceiling had caved in under the weight of the ash deposits, exposed areas of fresco were hit by falling debris. Deeper scratches could have been caused by collapsing roof beams (fig. 76). The ash rain was followed by the Peléan phase, an eruption lasting several hours during which glowing avalanches of hot ash, or nuées ardentes, streamed from the crater at enormous speed. There could have been several of these absolutely lethal pyroclastic flows of very hot volcanic gas and ash. In Herculaneum wood was heated to at least 750° Fahrenheit, and bones have been found that had been exposed to heat of more than 900°. It is more than likely that shutters and other wooden objects in the villa at Boscoreale were charred or burned, but accounts of the excavation fail to mention any such remnants.

The heat of the pyroclastic flows seems to have loosened plaster and paint, resulting in clearly discernible sequences of losses (see figs. 77, 78). Except for yellow ocher, the colors seem to have been unaffected by the heat. Yellow ocher when heated to at least 572° turns red. This chemical reaction in Pompeiian wall paintings is well documented, and the Metropolitan's panel with a garland from Room L of the Boscoreale villa (the exedra) contains a good example (fig. 79).

Further damage and losses must have occurred when the paintings were taken from the villa in the early twentieth century. Excavations at that time were far from scientific, and the method for the removal of wall paintings was less than perfect. A painting to be detached was faced by gluing cloth to the surface. The front was further reinforced with boards before the back of the fresco was cut away from the wall. (The original layer of plaster that remains with the Boscoreale paintings is

69–72. Clockwise from top left: frieze on a portal (cubiculum, panel F, left townscape); altar (panel B); monochrome yellow landscape (panel D, right of window); alcove window (panel F, right townscape). The many small figures in the frescoes in the cubiculum can be attributed to one painter.

73. Ancient repair, using the fresco technique, in panel B of the cubiculum, probably after the earthquake in A.D. 62

approximately ⅜ inch thick.) Once freed from the wall, the painting was laid facedown on the floor. A heavy chestnut frame with a wooden grid inserted in it and metal reinforcements was placed over the painting, and the wooden grid was filled in and covered with plaster. The thickness of the plaster bed depended on the size of the panel; for large panels it was approximately 6 inches deep. As the frescoes were detached original areas were lost. For instance, large parts of the six tall white pilasters in the cubiculum (see fig. 86) were sacrificed to extract the existing seven panels. The columns framing the Metropolitan's three panels from Room H (fig. 41) also seem to have been sacrificed, along with areas

74. Opening of the seam between two *giornate* in panel C of the cubiculum (see also fig. 62), probably after the earthquake in A.D. 62

75. Scratches in the fresco made by falling debris (cubiculum, panel B)

76. Deep scratch possibly made by a collapsing roof beam (cubiculum, panel F)

77–78. Sequences of losses in the frescoes in the cubiculum caused by pyroclastic flows of lava. Left: the east wall (panel B); right: the north wall, facing Mount Vesuvius, where hot debris apparently streamed through the window

from dado sections. There must be remnants of paintings in the villa, but the site was backfilled following the excavation in 1900.

During the recent reinstallation of the Metropolitan's Greek and Roman Galleries, the cubiculum was relocated to a gallery adjoining the eastern side of the Roman Court (fig. 80). The new location is the fourth since the fresco panels came to the Museum. Initially the cubiculum panels were installed in what was called the Roman Gallery, surrounded by other paintings from the villa (fig. 81). There was no ceiling, and black boards framed the panels. In 1909 a small annex adjoining the gallery was built for the cubiculum (fig. 82). Daylight came in through the window and through a skylight in the vaulted ceiling. There was a molding, and boards covered the edges of the panels. The cubiculum was again newly installed in 1963 in the southeastern part of the Great Hall (fig. 83). The bright red ceiling was vaulted in the area above the bed and flat over the rest of the room. Artificial light came through the window. The six tall pilasters dividing the scenes on the walls were restored according to photographs from the excavation (see figs. 84, 85). The imprecise placement of the panels was corrected in the most recent move. The room is now 2½ inches narrower and 2 inches shorter, and the painted walls are 1⅜

inches higher, although the original walls could not be reconstructed. The missing parts of the six pilasters were re-created (figs. 86–88), and the ceiling, which resembles that of the previous installation, was painted in light, neutral colors.

The condition of the paintings from Boscoreale ranges from beautifully preserved sections to fragile or badly damaged areas. For the latest reinstallation

79. Detail of a fresco fragment from the west wall of Room L of the villa (see fig. 31), where the heat of the pyroclastic flows turned the yellow ocher pigment to red

80. The cubiculum reinstalled in the New Greek and Roman Galleries, The Metropolitan Museum of Art, 2007 (for the frescoes, see also figs. 55–57)

81. First installation of the cubiculum in the Museum, in the former Roman Gallery, 1903 to 1909

82. Second installation of the cubiculum, in an annex adjoining the former Roman Gallery, 1909 to 1962

83. Third installation of the cubiculum, in the Great Hall, 1963 to 2004

41

84. West wall of the cubiculum in situ during the excavations at Boscoreale, ca. 1900

85. Northeast corner of the cubiculum in situ during the excavations at Boscoreale, ca. 1900. Photograph: Antikensammlung, Berlin

the panels in the Metropolitan were thoroughly restored. The campaign lasted, with some interruptions, from early 2002 to April 2007. The consolidation of brittle plaster and paint layers had become necessary. A cleaning of the frescoes was also overdue, and layers of dirt and wax or varnish that had accumulated over the years were cleaned away (see fig. 89). The inadequate inpainting of losses was removed as well. The latticework of the balustrade in panel D, for instance, had been wrongly restored with squares, and this was corrected by replacing the missing arches (figs. 90, 91).

A major part of the restoration focused on improving old fills of losses. For the initial restorations in Italy, cement had unfortunately been used as a filling material, producing unpleasant uneven surfaces with cement overlapping original paint. Many fills had cracked or lost sufficient adhesion and had to be replaced. Cement is not reversible, and it was only with great difficulty that necessary improvements could be made (figs. 92–95). The new

86. The pilaster between panels B and C in the cubiculum (see fig. 56) was sacrificed when the paintings were removed from the villa. The discrepancy in the heights of the panels was corrected in the new installation in 2007.

87 (far left). Pilaster between panels B and C in the cubiculum, during restoration

88 (left). Restored pilaster between panels B and C in the cubiculum, completed April 2007

89. Detail of a fresco fragment from the south wall of Room F of the villa (see fig. 47) during the removal of modern layers of wax and dirt

inpainting of losses was done in the so-called *tratteggio* manner, whereby the original painting is faithfully matched but with short, vertical brushstrokes so that at close range viewers can distinguish restorations from the ancient original (fig. 96).

Cement fills also obliterated the original window opening in the cubiculum, which must have contained a wooden frame with shutters. Thanks to the beveled edges on the frescoes that were revealed below the cement fills, the window's outlines could be reconstructed, although for safety reasons the modern frame could not be removed. There is sufficient evidence to reconstruct the window as comparable to the painted example with shutters on panel F in the cubiculum (fig. 97). This has been done in the virtual model (fig. 98), but it was decided not to install a modern reconstruction on the actual window opening. The model shows that with the frame

90–91. Detail of the balustrade in panel D of the cubiculum (see fig. 57), as it was previously incorrectly restored (above) and with the new inpainting completed in 2007 (below)

92. Cement fills in panel E of the cubiculum (see also fig. 55), before restoration

93–95. Detail of the center of the dado on panel F in the cubiculum (see also fig. 55), showing (top right) old fills of losses, including a large cement fill near the bottom; (left center) new fills of losses; and (right center) the completed restoration

96. Detail of a column capital on panel E in the cubiculum (see also fig. 55) that was restored in the *tratteggio* manner, in small vertical brush-strokes that are easily distinguished from the original painting

and shutters in place the composition of the wall decoration becomes remarkably more balanced. The grille that is on the window in the reconstructed cubiculum at the Metropolitan (see fig. 80) was reportedly found in the excavation, but it must have belonged elsewhere because it would not have fit into the cubiculum window with its wooden frame still intact.

97. Detail of a window and door with shutters on panel F in the cubiculum (see also fig. 55)

98. Virtual model of the Villa of P. Fannius Synistor, cubiculum, looking north (for the frescoes, see also figs. 55–57)

1. See Stefani 1994, pp. 86–92, and Casale and Bianco 1979, a pioneering contribution to understanding the topography of suburban Pompeii.
2. See Ruggiero 1888.
3. See De Caro 1994.
4. Zevi 1991, pp. 94–95.
5. See Rostovtzeff 1926, Carrington 1931, Day 1932, Castaldi 1950, Étienne 1982, D'Arms 1984, De Martino 1991, and Jashemski 1993.
6. Fergola et al. 2001, pp. 207–8, 217.
7. See the reports at http://www.fastionline.org/ record_view.php?fst_cd=AIAC_832.
8. Lupo 1991–92.
9. D'Agostino and Gastaldi 1979, Lepore 1989.
10. De Caro 1994, pp. 132–40, nos. 1–36, fig. 32.
11. Zevi 1982; Kockel 1986, pp. 546–47.
12. Zevi in De Caro 1994, p. 13.
13. De Caro 1999.
14. Tchernia 1986. For the suggestion that there was a *gens pompeiana* who were active in making and selling wine as early as the Samnite period, see Heurgon 1952 and Brun 2004, pp. 12ff. The opinions on this topic of Jongman (1988), who supposed that cereal production played a major role in the agriculture of Pompeii, are to be taken with a great deal of prudence.
15. Tchernia 1986, p. 176.
16. The story is told by Livy (Titus Livius; 59 B.C.–A.D. 17) in his history of Rome, *Ab urbe condita libri* (Books from the Foundation of the City, 2.8.4–5); by the Roman historian Lucius Annaeus Florus in *Epitome of Roman History* (2.8), compiled in the first or second century, chiefly from Livy; and by the Roman aristocrat Sextus Julius Frontinus (ca. A.D. 40–103) in his military treatise *Strategemata* (Stratagems, 1.5.21).
17. Cicirelli 1989.
18. Testament to this are the many small late Roman graves discovered at Boscoreale and Boscotrecase where the dead were interred in tile cists and cut African amphorae, with small stashes of oil lamps and money. See Cerulli Irelli 1975.
19. Jashemski in De Caro 1994, pp. 106–9.
20. Brendel 1954, p. 406.
21. The identities of the villa's owners remain unclear; see Herbert Bloch, "The Owners of the Villa near Boscoreale," in Lehmann 1953, pp. 214–17.
22. Barnabei (1901, p. 18) noted that only one small fresco fragment survived from the upper stories. Its whereabouts are unknown.
23. Stefani 2003, De Caro 1994. On the sizes of villas and groupings of rooms, see Dickmann 1999. D'Arms 1970 remains invaluable for a general understanding of the growth of the area under Roman rule.
24. Drerup 1957. On *luxus*, or the concept of luxury, in imperial Rome, see Dubois-Pellerin 2008.
25. O'Sullivan 2006.
26. McEwen 2003. The effects of these principles on Second Style painting have been much discussed, notably in Beyen 1938–60, Tybout 1989, and Ehrhardt 1991, pp. 42–46.
27. Similar garlands appear in sculpture and painting in the so-called House of Augustus on the Palatine Hill in Rome (Carettoni 1983, Settis 1988). Castriota (1995, p. 29) identifies such copious garlands as "pankarpia." On the three garlands from Villa Kérylos, see Barbet 2009.
28. Bounia 2004, Bergmann 1995. On new modes in art and literature in the Late Republic, see Grüner 2004.
29. The finds are listed in Oettel 1996, pp. 272–73.
30. Lehmann 1953, p. 13.
31. The farm tools and other bronze and iron implements belong to the Field Museum in Chicago (De Cou 1912, pp. 208–11).
32. On the popular pairing of Venus and Bacchus in Roman art, see Zanker 1998.
33. The comparable *megalographia* was found at the Villa dei Misteri in Pompeii in the early 1900s, a few years after the discovery of this villa. More recently, strikingly similar paintings, however with smaller figures, were found in a rustic villa at Terzigno (Moormann 2006, Strocka 2005–6).
34. Müller 1994, Smith 1994, Virgilio 2000, Torelli 2003 (with earlier bibliography), Sauron 2007.
35. Cagiano de Azevedo 1952, Verbanck-Piérard 2008.
36. Beyen (1938–60, vol. 1, pp. 223–27) recognized some mistakes in Barnabei's drawing of the west wall. On the red monochromes, see Bruno 1993.
37. That nearly identical objects and sections of painted architecture appear in the Casa del Labirinto and the Villa dei Misteri at Pompeii and in the villa at Oplontis attests to the use of adaptable schemes by fresco workshops (Bragantini 2004, Strocka 1991, De Franciscis 1975; and see http:// www.oplontisproject.org/index.html).
38. Similar monochrome landscapes on yellow panels appear in the Casa di Livia on the Palatine in Rome and in Triclinium 14 of the villa at Oplontis. On the ambiguity of painted views, see Drerup 1959, Scagliarini Corlàita 1974–76, Bek 1980, and Bergmann 2002b.
39. On the miniature monochrome friezes as depictions of Dionysiac rituals, see Turcan 1993. On the phalluses, see Turcan 1960, especially p. 177.
40. The heated debate about whether the frescoes depict theater, palace, or villa has subsided lately, with scholars acknowledging multiple associations and a pervasive "theatricality" in the decor. Columns "gilded and studded with gems and silvered" supported a pavilion of Alexander, while golden columns entwined with tendrils of golden acanthus decorated his hearse (Diodorus Siculus, Library 18.272, Athenaeus, *Banquet of the Learned* 12.538d). On architectural precedents in Alexandria, see McKenzie 2007, pp. 80–118, and McKenzie 1995. On the popularity of theater motifs, see Webster 1995. On the absorption of sacred into private land, see Coarelli 1983. On the new luxury in Roman home building, see Wiseman 1987. In Book 6 of his *De architectura*, Vitruvius recommended that elite Romans emulate public architecture in their homes.
41. Lavagne 1988, Bergmann 2002a.

Anderson, Maxwell L. "Pompeian Frescoes in The Metropolitan Museum of Art." *The Metropolitan Museum of Art Bulletin* 45, no. 3 (Winter 1987–88).

Andreae, Bernard. "Rekonstruktion des grossen Oecus der Villa des P. Fannius Synistor in Boscoreale." In *Neue Forschungen in Pompeji*, edited by Bernard Andreae and Helmut Kyrieleis, pp. 71–92. Recklinghausen, 1975.

Barbet, Alix. "Les peintures romaines inédites de la Villa Kérylos." *Cahiers de la Villa "Kérylos"* (Paris) 20 (2009), pp. 51–67.

Barnabei, Felice. *La Villa Pompeiana di P. Fannio Sinistore scoperta presso Boscoreale*. Rome: Accademia dei Lincei, 1901.

Bek, Lise. *Towards Paradise on Earth: Modern Space Conception in Architecture; a Creation of Renaissance Humanism*. [Odense, Denmark], 1980.

Bergmann, Bettina. "Greek Masterpieces and Roman Recreative Fictions." In "Greece in Rome: Influence, Integration, Resistance," edited by Charles Segal, *Harvard Studies in Classical Philology* 97 (1995), pp. 79–120.

———. "Art and Nature in the Villa at Oplontis." *Journal of Roman Archaeology, Supplementary Series*, no. 47 (2002a), pp. 87–120.

———. "Playing with Boundaries: Painted Architecture in Roman Interiors." In *The Built Surface*, vol. 1, *Architecture and the Pictorial Arts from Antiquity to the Enlightenment*, edited by Christy Anderson, pp. 15–46. Aldershot, England, 2002b.

Beyen, Hendrik Gerard. *Die pompejanische Wanddekoration, vom zweiten bis zum vierten Stil*. 2 vols. The Hague, 1938–60.

Blümner, Hugo. *Technologie und Terminologie der Gewerbe und Künste bei Griechen und Römern*. Vol. 3. Leipzig, 1884.

Bounia, Alexandra. *The Nature of Classical Collecting: Collectors and Collections, 100 BCE–100 CE*. Aldershot, England, 2004.

Bragantini, Irene. "La produzione della parietale romana." *Journal of Roman Archaeology* 17 (2004), pp. 131–45.

Brendel, Otto J. Review of Lehmann 1953. *American Journal of Philology* 75 (1954), pp. 406–10.

Brun, Jean-Pierre. *L'archéologie du vin et de l'huile dans l'Empire romain*. Paris, 2004.

Bruno, Vincent. "Mark Rothko and the Second Style: The Art of the Color-Field in Roman Murals." In *Eius Virtutis Studiosi: Classical and Postclassical Studies in Memory of Frank Edward Brown (1908–1988)*, edited by Russell T. Scott and Ann Reynolds Scott, pp. 235–55. Washington, D.C., 1993.

Cagiano de Azevedo, Michelangelo. "Il restauro degli affreschi romani del museo di Mariemont (Belgio)." *Bollettino dell'Istituto Centrale del Restauro*, no. 11–12 (1952), pp. 159–79.

Carettoni, Gianfilippo. *Das Haus des Augustus auf dem Palatin*. Mainz, 1983.

Carrington, R. C. "Studies in the Campanian 'villae rusticae.'" *Journal of Roman Studies* 21 (1931), pp. 110–30.

Casale, Angelandrea, and Angelo Bianco. "Primo contributo alla topografia del suburbio Pompeiano." *Antiqua*, suppl. 15 (October–December 1979), pp. 27–56.

Castaldi, F. "La trasformazione della 'villa rustica' romana in rapporto alle condizioni dell'agricoltura." *Annali del Pontificio Istituto Superiore di Scienze e Lettere S. Chiara*, 1950, pp. 269–78.

Castriota, David. *The Ara Pacis Augustae and the Imagery of Abundance in Later Greek and Early Roman Imperial Art*. Princeton, 1995.

Cerulli Irelli, G. "Intorno al problema della rinascita di Pompei." In *Neue Forschungen in Pompeji und den anderen vom Vesuvausbruch 79 n. Chr. verschütteten Städten*, edited by Bernard Andreae, pp. 291–98. Recklinghausen, 1975.

Cicirelli, Caterina, ed. *La ville romane di Terzigno*. Terzigno, 1989.

Cirillo, Antonio, and Angelandrea Casale. *Il Tesoro di Boscoreale e il suo scopritore: La vera storia ricostruita sui documenti dell'epoca*. Pompeii, 2004.

Coarelli, Filippo. "Architettura sacra e architettura privata nella tarda repubblica." In *Architecture et société: De l'archaïsme grec à la fin de la République romaine*, pp. 191–217. Rome and Paris, 1983.

Cook, Brian F. "The Boscoreale Cubiculum: A New Installation." *The Metropolitan Museum of Art Bulletin*, n.s., 22 (January 1964), pp. 166–83.

D'Agostino, Bruno, and P. Gastaldi. "Le necropoli protostoriche della valle del Sarno." *AION, Annali dell'Istituto Universitario Orientale di Napoli* 1 (1979), pp. 13–57.

D'Arms, John H. *Romans on the Bay of Naples: A Social and Cultural Study of the Villas and Their Owners from 150 B.C. to A.D. 400*. Cambridge, Mass., 1970.

———. "Ville rustiche e ville di 'otium.'" *Pompei 79* (1984), pp. 65ff.

Day, John. "Agriculture in the Life of Pompeii." *Yale Classical Studies* 3 (1932), pp. 166–208.

De Caro, Stefano. *La villa rustica in località Villa Regina a Boscoreale*. Rome, 1994.

———. "Vesuvio-Monte Somma (NA): Iscrizione osca su un termine." *Studi Etruschi—Rivista di Epigrafia Italica*, ser. 3, 63 (1999), pp. 456–61.

De Cou, Herbert F. *Antiquities from Boscoreale in the Field Museum of Natural History*. Field Museum of Natural History, Publication 152. Chicago, 1912.

De Franciscis, Alfonso. *The Pompeian Wall Paintings in the Roman Villa of Oplontis*. Recklinghausen, 1975.

De Martino, Francesco. "Attività economica e realtà sociale." In *Storia e civiltà della Campania*, vol. 1, *L'evo antico*, edited by Giovanni Pugliese Carratelli, pp. 193–233. Naples, 1991.

Dickmann, Jens-Arne. *Domus frequentata: Anspruchsvolles Wohnen im pompejanischen Stadthaus*. 2 vols. Munich, 1999.

Drerup, Heinrich. *Zum Ausstattungsluxus in der römischen Architektur: Ein formgeschichtlicher Versuch*. Münster, 1957.

———. "Bildraum und Realraum in der römischen Architektur." *Mitteilungen des Deutschen Archäologischen Instituts: Römische Abteilung* 66 (1959), pp. 147–74.

Dubois-Pellerin, Éva. *Le luxe privé à Rome et en Italie au Ier siècle après J.-C.* Naples, 2008.

Ehrhardt, Wolfgang. "Bild und Ausblick in Wand-bemalungen Zweiten Stils." *Antike Kunst* 34 (1991), pp. 28–65.

Étienne, Robert. "Villas du Vésuve et structure agraire." In *La regione sotterrata dal Vesuvio: Studi e prospettive nazionale, 11–15 n* Naples, 1982.

Fergola, L., et al. "Recenti indagini geoarcheologiche nei territori di Boscoreale." In *Pompei. Scienza e Società, Atti del Convegno Internazionale per il 250 Anniversario degli Scavi di Pompei, Napoli 25–27 novembre 1998*, edited by P. G. Guzzo, pp. 207–17. Milan, 2001.

Grüner, Andreas. *Venus ordinis: Der Wandel von Malerei und Literatur im Zeitalter der römischen Bürgerkriege*. Paderborn, 2004.

Heurgon, Jacques. "Les Lassii pompéiens et l'importation des vins italiens en Gaule." *La parola del passato* 7 (1952), pp. 113–18.

Jashemski, Wilhelmina F. *The Gardens of Pompeii: Herculaneum and the Villas Destroyed by Vesuvius*. Vol. 2. New Rochelle, N.Y., 1993.

Jongman, Willem. *The Economy and Society of Pompeii*. Amsterdam, 1988.

Kockel, Valentin. "Archäologische Funde und Forschungen in dem Vesuvstädten, II." *Archäologischer Anzeiger*, 1986, pp. 443–569.

Kolendo, Jerzy. *L'agricoltura nell'Italia romana: Tecniche agrarie e progresso economico dalla tarda repubblica al principato*. Translated by Celeste Zawadzka. Rome, 1980.

Lavagne, Henri. *Operosa Antra: Recherches sur la grotte à Rome de Sylla à Hadrien*. Rome, 1988.

Lehmann, Phyllis Williams. *Roman Wall Paintings from Boscoreale in the Metropolitan Museum of Art*. With an appendix by Herbert Bloch. Cambridge, 1953.

Lepore, Ettore. *Origini e strutture della Campania antica: Saggi di storia etno-sociale*. Bologna, 1989.

Ling, Roger. *Roman Painting*. Cambridge, 1991.

Lupo, I. "Materiali archeologici di età preromana nella biblioteca comunale di Boscoreale." *Rendiconti della Accademia di Archeologia, Lettere e Belle Arti di Napoli* 63 (1991–92), pp. 499–538.

McEwen, Indra Kagis. *Vitruvius: Writing the Body of Architecture*. Cambridge, Mass., 2003.

McKenzie, Judith. *The Architecture of Petra*. Reprint. Oxford, 1995. Originally published 1990.

———. *The Architecture of Alexandria and Egypt, c. 300 B.C. to A.D. 700*. New Haven, 2007.

Mielsch, Harald. *Römische Wandmalerei*. Darmstadt, 2001.

Moormann, Eric M. "Une épopée peinte sur les parois: La 'mégalographie' de Terzigno (Pompéi, Ier s. av. J.-C.)." *Les dossiers d'archéologie*, no. 318 (2006), pp. 26–29.

Mora, Paolo, Laura Mora, and Paul Philippot. *Conservation of Wall Paintings*. London, 1984.

Müller, Frank G. J. M. *The Wall Paintings from the Oecus of the Villa of Publius Fannius Synistor in Boscoreale*. Amsterdam, 1994.

Oettel, Andreas. *Fundkontexte römischer Vesuvvillen im Gebiet um Pompeji: Die Grabungen von 1894 bis 1908*. Mainz, 1996.

O'Sullivan, Timothy M. "The Mind in Motion: Walking and Metaphorical Travel in the Roman Villa." *Classical Philology* 101 (2006), pp. 133–52.

Poli Capri, Paola, ed. *Pompei: I tesori di Boscoreale; lettere e documenti*. 5 vols. Rome, 2001.

Purcell, N. "Wine and Wealth in Ancient Italy." *Journal of Roman Studies* 75 (1985), pp. 1–19.

Rostovtzeff, Michael Ivanovitch. *The Social and Economic History of the Roman Empire*. Oxford, 1926.

Ruggiero, Michele. *Degli scavi di antichità nelle province di Terraferma dell'antico regno di Napoli dal 1743 al 1876*. Naples, 1888.

Sambon, Arthur. *Catalogue des fresques de Boscoreale*. Sale, Galeries Durand-Ruel, Paris, June 8, 1903.

Sampaolo, Valeria, and Irene Bragantini, eds. *La pittura pompeiana*. Naples, 2009.

Sauron, Gilles. *La peinture allégorique à Pompéi: Le regard de Cicéron*. Paris, 2007.

Scagliarini Corlàita, Daniela. "Spazio e decorazione nella pittura pompeiana." *Palladio* 23–25 (1974–76), pp. 3–44.

Settis, Salvatore. "Die Ara Pacis." In *Kaiser Augustus und die verlorene Republik*, pp. 400–426. Exh. cat., Martin-Gropius-Bau, Berlin. Mainz, 1988.

Sigurdsson, Haraldur, Stanford Cashdollar, and Stephen R. J. Sparks. "The Eruption of Vesuvius in A.D. 79: Reconstruction from Historical and Volcanological Evidence." *American Journal of Archaeology* 86 (1982), pp. 39–51.

Smith, R. R. R. "Spear-won Land at Boscoreale: On the Royal Paintings of a Roman Villa." *Journal of Roman Archaeology* 7 (1994), pp. 100–128.

Stefani, Grete. *Pompei. Vecchi scavi sconosciuti: La villa rinvenuta dal marchese Giovanni Imperiali in località Civita (1907–1908)*. Rome, 1994.

———, as ed. *Uomo e ambiente nel territorio vesuviano: Guida all'Antiquarium di Boscoreale*. Pompeii, 2003.

Strocka, Volker Michael. *Casa del Labirinto (VI 11, 8–10)*. Häuser in Pompeji 4. Munich, 1991.

———. "Troja—Karthago—Rom: Ein vorvergilisches Bildprogramm in Terzigno bei Pompeji." *Mitteilungen des Deutschen Archäologischen Instituts: Römische Abteilung* 112 (2005–6), pp. 79–120.

Tchernia, André. *Le vin de l'Italie romaine: Essai d'histoire économique d'après les amphores*. Rome, 1986.

Torelli, Mario. "The Frescoes of the Great Hall of the Villa at Boscoreale: Iconography and Politics." In *Myth, History and Culture in Republican Rome: Studies in Honour of T. P. Wiseman*, edited by David Braund and Christopher Gill, pp. 217–56. Exeter, 2003.

Turcan, Robert. "Priapea." *Mélanges de l'École Française de Rome* 72 (1960), pp. 167–89.

———. "Les petites frises du cubiculum M dans la Villa dite de P. Fannius Synistor à Boscoreale (New York, Metropolitan Museum)." *Comptes rendus des séances de l'Académie des Inscriptions et Belles-Lettres* (1993), pp. 701–22.

Tybout, Rolf A. *Aedificiorum figurae: Untersuchungen zu den Architekturdarstellungen des frühen zweiten Stils*. Amsterdam, 1989.

Verbanck-Piérard, Annie. "Trésor de Mariemont." *Cahiers de Mariemont* 37–38 (2008).

Virgilio, Biagio. "Re e regalità ellenistica negli affreschi di Boscoreale." In *Donum natalicium: Studi presentati a Claudio Saporetti in occasione del suo 60. compleanno*, pp. 295–312. Rome, 2000.

Webster, T. B. L. *Monuments Illustrating New Comedy*. 3rd ed., revised by J. R. Green and A. Seeberg. 2 vols. London, 1995.

Wiseman, T. P. "*Conspicui postes tectaque digna deo*: The Public Image of Aristocratic Houses in the Late Republic and Early Empire." In *L'Urbs: Espace urbain et histoire (Ier siècle av. J.C.–IIIe siècle ap. J.C.)*, pp. 393–413. Rome, 1987.

Zanker, Paul. *Eine Kunst für die Sinne: Zur hellenistischen Bilderwelt des Dionysos und der Aphrodite*. Berlin, 1998.

Zevi, Fausto. "Urbanistica di Pompei." In *La regione sotterrata dal Vesuvio: Studi e prospettive, Atti del Convegno Internazionale, 11–15 novembre 1979*, pp. 353–66. Naples, 1982.

———, as ed. *Pompei*. Vol. 1. Naples, 1991.

48